MW01056645

THE LITTLE ONES WHO CAME

CHILDREN WHO WITNESSED THE RESURRECTION

THE EYEWITNESSES
BOOK FOUR

KENNETH A WINTER

Illustrated by
CARLEY ELDER

WildernessLessons

The Little Ones Who Came

Children who witnessed the Resurrection

The Eyewitnesses Collection – Book 4

Published by:

Kenneth A. Winter

WildernessLessons, LLC

Richmond, Virginia

United States of America

kenwinter.org

wildernesslessons.com

Illustrated by Carley Elder

Edited by Sheryl Martin Hash

Cover design by Dennis Waterman

ISBN 978-1-7349345-5-7 (hard cover)

ISBN 978-1-7349345-6-4 (soft cover)

ISBN 978-1-7349345-7-1 (e-book)

Library of Congress Control Number: 2020925480

DEDICATION

In memory of
Harry and Sara Winter
(my grandparents)

for their investment in the lives of so many little ones
who, as a result, came to know Jesus.

But Jesus said, "Let the little children come to Me,
and do not forbid them; for of such is the kingdom of
heaven."
(Matthew 19:14 NKJ)

CONTENTS

FROM THE AUTHOR

～

The stories in this book are a mixture of fact and fiction. They are fictional, eyewitness accounts from young men and women who witnessed events surrounding the ministry, death, and resurrection of Jesus. At the end of each story is a brief explanation to help you clearly understand what is fiction and what is fact.

My prayer is that through these stories you will begin to see the events surrounding the life, death, and resurrection of Jesus in a new way – and perhaps through different eyes. Hopefully, you will see the miracles that Jesus performed, the truth He taught, and the lives He changed. Though the children telling their stories are fictional, they reveal the truth of who Jesus is, why He came, and the difference He makes in our lives.

The lives of family, friends, neighbors, and even total strangers were changed by Jesus through the faithful obedience of those who followed Him. You will read how the young men and women could have been used to play a role in the Gospel story – just like you and i have an opportunity to play a role in that same story.

Throughout your life, God will call you to do something that will require the faith and obedience you read about in these stories – like that demonstrated by Simon Peter and his family, Lazarus and his sisters, and others that we read about in the Bible. i hope you will be like the young men and women in this book who know the truth and act on it faithfully.

Finally, throughout all of the stories in this book, you will find Jesus. My prayer is that you won't only know *about* Him, you will come to know Him personally. Jesus said, *"Let the little children come to Me. Don't stop them. The kingdom of God belongs to people who are like these little children. I tell you the truth. You must accept the kingdom of God as a little child accepts things, or you will never enter it."*[1]

That's why the title of this book is ***"The Little Ones Who Came."*** It's not really about how old they are. We must all come to Jesus with faith like children. We're never too old ... and we're never too young. i'm a ***little one who came*** to Jesus, because i came with the faith of a little child, even though i was thirty-six years old at the time.

We all have sinned – everyone who has ever walked on the face of this earth – except Jesus![2] Jesus died on the cross to pay the price for our sins. And then He rose from the dead as our Living Savior[3]. He is still very much alive, and He wants to have a personal relationship with each and every one of us.[4]

If you are not already a believer, i pray that you will become one today. Accept Him as your Savior,[5] as He said, *"just like a little child accepts things."* Then you, too, will be one of ... **The Little Ones Who Came**.

Sarah and and her sister, Iscah, wave goodbye to
their father along the Sea of Galilee as he leaves to
follow Jesus.

SARAH, THE DAUGHTER OF SIMON PETER

*H*i, my name is Sarah. My mother's name is Gabriella and my father's name was Simon. But a little over three years ago, Jesus gave my dad a second name. He said my dad would also be called Peter, which means "a rock." It wasn't only my dad's name that was changed that day – so was he!

My dad and his brother, my uncle Andrew, grew up as fishermen, just like my grandfather. It was uncle Andrew who first introduced my dad to Jesus. I was twelve years old when Jesus came to our fishing village along the Sea of Galilee. Even back then, large crowds of people would gather to hear Jesus teach. There were so many that day that Jesus stepped into my dad's boat and asked that it be pushed out into the water so He could speak to all of the people gathered along the shore. My mom, my younger sister Iscah, and I were standing among the crowd.

My dad brought Jesus back to shore after He finished speaking. When Jesus stepped out of the boat, He told my dad to take it back out to the deeper water and let down his fishing nets. My dad, my uncle, and their partners had been fishing all night. They hadn't caught any fish and now they were ready to go home and rest because they were tired. But my dad said, *"Master, we worked hard all night trying to catch fish, but we caught nothing. But You say to put the nets in the water; so I will."*[1]

When they lowered their nets into the water, they immediately filled with fish. There were so many fish they couldn't pull the nets into the boat. My dad yelled to the other men on shore to come help them. Later my dad told me that in all of his years of fishing, he had never seen that many fish fill a net. He said he thought the nets were going to break or the boat was going to sink because there were so many!

When they finally made it back to shore, my dad jumped out of the boat, fell to his knees before Jesus, and said, *"Go away from me, Lord. I am a sinful man!"*[2] But Jesus didn't judge my dad for being a sinner. Instead He said, *"Don't be afraid. From now on you will be fishermen for men."*[3]

Earlier that week I had overheard my parents talking. My dad said, "Gabriella, I believe Jesus is the Promised One. Though we only just met, I believe He knows me better than I know myself. I believe my life will be different because of Him. I believe all of our lives will be different because of Him!"

"Have you wondered if you are supposed to travel with Him and become one of His disciples?" my mom asked.

. . .

"I can't just leave and follow Him," my dad replied. "I can't abandon you and the girls or my business partner. God has called me to be your husband, a father to Sarah and Iscah, and a partner to Zebedee. I cannot turn my back on all of you or what God has called me to do."

"You are a man of honor, Simon," my mom said. "That's one of the many reasons I love you. And I know you will never abandon me or your family. But I also know that if God calls you to follow Jesus, you must do so. And we must all trust God to take care of us. His call on one of our lives is a call of obedience on all of us. If God so leads, the girls and I will go live with my mother. We will be fine. We will trust God – and you must also! Let us watch and see how God leads!"

Now, as I stood there watching my father kneeling before Jesus, I knew that he needed to leave us and go follow Jesus. I knew life would be different for our family. We would move to a new place. My dad would be gone for long periods at a time. But I knew in my heart that was what we were all supposed to do. I looked up at my mom. I could see a small tear in the corner of her eye. But I also saw her smile as she nodded at my dad. They both knew he needed to go with Jesus.

Many of our good friends and family left our hometown that day to follow Jesus. The group included my dad, my uncle Andrew, my uncle Thomas (my mom's twin brother), my dad's partners, James and John; Zebedee's wife, Salome; and two of the other fishermen, Philip and Bartholomew. My mom, Iscah, and I joined the others standing on the shore as they watched their family members and friends leave. We were sad to say farewell, but we knew we were doing what God wanted us to do – both those who were going and those left behind.

Later that day, Zebedee came by to see us. He wanted mom to know that he had made an agreement with my dad to provide the money we would need to live on. He didn't want her to worry about money. He explained that he believed Jesus had called him to stay behind to run the fishing business so that our needs, and the needs of the families of the others who had left that day to follow Jesus, would be met. It was another reminder that all of us are to be followers of Jesus – but we all play different parts.

It didn't take long for Iscah and me to help our mom pack up our belongings. Within a week after my dad left, we moved to a town called Capernaum. It was only about six miles away, so we arrived at our new home later that same day. We would now be living with my grandmother – my mom's mother, whose name is Milcah.

My new home is also a fishing village, but it is much larger than where I came from. It feels more like a busy city than a sleepy village. Iscah and I began to make new friends our first week here. One of those friends is Ilana, the daughter of our rabbi, Jairus. Ilana is two years younger than I am.

A few months after we moved here, Jesus and His followers came for a visit. We were so happy to have my dad home for a few days. My grandmother was also glad to have her son, my uncle Thomas, home, too. My mom and grandmother got busy preparing meals for the other people who were traveling with Jesus. Iscah and I helped as much as we could. Though some of Jesus's followers had family here in the village, most of them did not. So they always stayed with us whenever they were in town. Salome and the other women who were traveling with Jesus also stepped right in to help us prepare meals.

Two days after everyone arrived, I was helping in the kitchen when my grandmother fell on the floor. She had not felt good since the day before, but she had not told anyone. My mom ran to help her and quickly realized my grandmother was burning up with fever. My mom told me to run get my dad who was with

Jesus in the synagogue (a place where Jewish people meet to worship and pray to God).

When I arrived, I saw Ilana. I told her what had happened, and she took me to my dad. My dad told Jesus about my grandmother and they, along with Ilana's dad, quickly headed to our house. Ilana and I had to run to keep up with them!

Dad led Jesus to my grandmother's bedroom where my mom and the other women were standing around her. Everyone turned to look at Jesus as He walked into the room. He went to the side of the bed and looked down at my grandmother. We all wondered what He was going to do. I had heard my mom and dad talk about the way Jesus made sick people well, but I had never seen Him do it. I prayed that He would make my grandmother better.

Suddenly, I realized that Jesus had turned to look at me. He smiled at me and nodded His head. It was as if He knew what I was praying.

Then He reached down and touched my grandmother's hand. Right away, her fever left, and her temperature returned to normal. She sat up as if nothing had been wrong with her! After a couple of minutes, she looked at my mom and said, "Gabriella, it looks like everyone has arrived for dinner. Let's get the food on the table!"

With that, she got up and went about her work. I'm not sure if she really understood that Jesus had healed her … but the rest of us did. From that moment on, everything we did was our way of saying "thank you" to Jesus.

Later that day, Jesus told me He had heard my prayer asking Him to help my grandmother. "Sarah," He said, "if you ask according to My will and *have faith, and do not doubt, you will get anything you ask for in prayer.*"[(4)] Then He turned to my dad and Rabbi Jairus and said, "*I tell you the truth. You must accept the kingdom of God as a little child accepts things, or you will never enter it.*"[(5)]

. . .

Jesus often returned to our fishing village, which meant we were able to see my dad often as well. Each time he returned home, daddy told us about the great things that Jesus had done. We could also tell that my dad's life was changing. He was becoming more like Jesus. So, that was a goal I set for myself. No matter our age, all of us who love Jesus should try to be more like Him.

One day my dad told us about the night he walked on water! I could not believe it! He said Jesus told him and His other followers to take their boat and cross to the other side of the lake. But soon the sea became rough and the wind began to blow. All the men were rowing as hard as they could, but the storm was slowing them down. Suddenly, they saw someone walking toward them. They got scared because they thought it was a ghost. But Jesus spoke to them and said, *"Take heart; it is I. Do not be afraid."*[6]

My dad cried out to Jesus, *"Lord, if it is You, command me to come to You on the water."*[7]

. . .

Jesus answered, *"Come."*[8]

So my dad got out of the boat and walked on the water toward Jesus. But when he took his eyes off of Jesus and looked at the wind and the sea, he became afraid and began to sink. He cried out, *"Lord, save me."*[9]

Jesus reached out, took hold of my dad's hand, and led him back to the boat. As soon as they got into the boat, the wind stopped blowing. Jesus looked at my dad and said, *"O you of little faith, why did you doubt?"*[10]

What happened to my dad made me think about what Jesus said to me when He healed my grandmother: *"Have faith, and do not doubt!"*[11] I think that's a good lesson for all of us to learn – no matter how old or young we are!

There have been many more lessons … and many more miracles over the past three years. Today, I'm standing on a hill with my dad. Jesus is leaving. He is returning to heaven. But He told all of us to share the lessons He taught us with others. We are to tell them to believe in Jesus just like a little one. I know how to do that … because I'm a little one who came.

More about Sarah

Sarah is not in the Bible, neither is her sister Iscah, but her father Simon Peter is. He was one of Jesus's closest followers. The Bible doesn't tell us anything about his wife or if they had any children. It is, however, very likely that they did. We know that he was married and that he grew up and lived in Bethsaida before Jesus renamed him Peter and called him to follow Him. We know that Peter's mother-in-law lived in Capernaum, and Jesus healed her.

You can read in the Bible about how Jesus healed Peter's mother-in-law in Matthew 8:14-15 and about the night Peter walked on the water in Matthew 14:22-33.

~

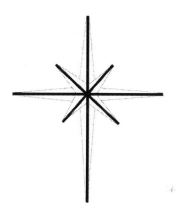

Ruth, at her sister's wedding, watches the servants
fill the water pots as Jesus has told them.

RUTH, THE DAUGHTER OF SALOME

*M*y name is Ruth and I am twelve years old. My mother's name is Salome and my father's name is Joachim. I am the youngest in my family. My sister, Mary, is the oldest and we have two brothers between us in age.

Jesus's mom, Mary, and my mom are best friends. As a matter of fact, we grew up calling her Dohdah, which means "aunt." Dohdah is also my sister's godmother and namesake. Though my family and Jesus's family lived in different villages, we were only about an hour apart, so we saw each other often. That is, until

Dohdah recently moved to a village farther away called Capernaum.

I have known Jesus all of my life. I don't remember His father, Joseph. I'm told he died soon after I was born. So Jesus has always been the man of His family for as long as I have known Him. Even when I was little, Jesus always took time to talk with me. He once gave me a doll He had made Himself. The doll is my most treasured possession. He told me the doll's name was Ruth, just like mine.

Jesus said He named the doll after a woman who had lived a long time ago. Her husband died while she was still young, and she lost almost everything she had. All she had left was her husband's mother, whom she loved dearly, and her trust in God. Jesus told me that God rewarded Ruth's faith and her devotion, and she became the great-grandmother of the greatest king of Israel – King David. He told me to remember that whenever I hear my name – God always rewards faith and trust in Him.

· · ·

Over three years ago, my sister married her husband, Jacob. Mary was a beautiful bride and it was a beautiful day. It was the first time I ever attended a wedding, and I could not imagine anything more wonderful. My father spent a lot of money! Friends and family came from all over to attend the wedding. There was plenty of good food, delicious desserts, and joyful music.

My dad had arranged for his best friend to act as the master of ceremonies, whose job was to make sure that everything took place on time. We had grown up calling him uncle Samuel, even though he wasn't really our uncle. He paid attention to everything that was going on at the wedding so my parents could pay attention to greeting their many guests.

Dohdah and all of her children, except Jesus, were some of the first to arrive. She told my mom not to worry about anything. She would help uncle Samuel make sure everything went smoothly. Dohdah and my mom always helped each other out like that.

· · ·

Jesus arrived a little later, together with several of His friends. Dohdah's face glowed as her oldest son entered the courtyard. He smiled and hugged His mother before saying hello to the rest of us. He told my parents that He hoped it was all right that He brought some friends along. My mom told them she was happy to have them, and they should make themselves at home. Our whole family was glad Jesus could be there for the wedding. He had the ability to brighten a room just by being there.

Since it was my first wedding, I didn't want to miss anything. I ate a little of all the good food. I smiled as I listened to the music and laughter. I enjoyed watching the dancing. My mother even told both of my brothers to dance with me.

Later that afternoon, I noticed Dohdah had gathered several of the servants, along with Jesus, and He was giving them instructions. They were standing near the large jars of water that our guests used to wash their hands and feet when they arrived. I guessed the water had run dry and the servants were refilling the jars.

.   .   .

But then I saw something surprising. One of the servants put some of the water into a cup and took it to uncle Samuel. I don't know why they wanted uncle Samuel to drink water that was supposed to be used for washing hands and feet!

After taking a drink from the cup, uncle Samuel quickly walked over to my dad. I wasn't sure what was going on, but by now I was really curious. I was afraid uncle Samuel was going to complain that the servants had given him a cup of unclean water. But instead he told my dad, "*A host always serves the best wine first. Then, when everyone has had a lot to drink, he brings out the less expensive wine. But you have kept the best until now!*"[1]

What was uncle Samuel talking about? The servants hadn't put wine in the cup; it was water from the jars. Why was he saying that this was the best wine? I looked over at my mom. She was looking at Dohdah, who was looking at

Jesus. What had Jesus done? Everyone, except Jesus, looked shocked.

I decided I needed to find out what was going on, so I walked over to Dohdah and asked her. "You don't miss anything, Ruth," she laughed. "The servants told me we were running out of wine. There were many more guests than your parents had expected! Running out of food or drink would be embarrassing for your parents. So, I asked Jesus for His help.

"At first, Jesus said, '*Why come to Me? My time has not yet come.*'[2] But I told the servants to do whatever He told them. I knew He could solve the problem!

"Jesus told the servants to fill all six of the stone jars with water. Then He told them to dip out some of the water from one of the jars and take it to your uncle Samuel. And the rest you know!"

. . .

"But how did the servants know that Jesus had turned the water into wine?" I asked.

Dohdah looked at me and smiled. "Because they had faith and trusted Him!" Then I watched as she turned to look at Jesus across the room, and He smiled back at His mother.

A few months later, Jesus and His followers were again traveling through our village. He stopped to spend the night with our family. The number of people who were traveling with Him had grown a lot since the wedding. As always, our family was so glad to see Him!

Soon after He had arrived, Jesus, His followers, and my family were all sitting in the yard when a man asked to enter our home. Even I could tell from the way he was dressed that he was an official of King Herod's court. He introduced himself to Jesus and said his name was Chuza. It was unusual for one of King Herod's officials to come to our village, let alone our home. At first, my dad thought we had done something wrong!

. . .

But quickly the man began to tell Jesus that his son, who was just a year older than me, was very sick. The doctors had said his son was going to die soon. The man explained that he had heard Jesus could make sick people well again. He and his wife had brought the boy to Capernaum to find Jesus. But when they arrived, they were told Jesus was not there. The boy was too sick to travel any farther, so the father had come on alone to get Jesus and take Him back to his son. He explained that the boy did not have much time to live.

It was already one o'clock in the afternoon, and it would take a full day to get to the sick child. So, the official begged Jesus to return with him right then to heal his son. I could see the fear in the man's eyes and hear it in his voice. He believed Jesus was his only hope to save his son.

I thought Jesus was going to leave with the man right away. But instead, Jesus asked a question to all of us. *"Why must you people see signs and miracles before you will believe in Me?"*[3]

The official begged, *"Sir, please come before my child dies."*[4]

Jesus felt sorry for the man and told him, *"Go. Your son will live."*[5]

I wondered what the man was going to do. Would he keep begging Jesus to return with him? Or would he try to use his position as an official in Herod's court to order Jesus to come with him? But none of those things happened. The man trusted Jesus and believed what He had said. He turned and began his trip back to his son.

Jesus looked at us and praised the man for his faith. I knew that just as Jesus had turned water into wine, that sick boy was now well. His father had shown the same faith in Jesus that the servants had shown at my sister's wedding.

. . .

A few weeks later, my mom and I went to visit Dohdah in Capernaum. While we were there, I found out that the sick boy had been healed. As a matter of fact, the news had spread throughout the village that his fever disappeared at the same time Jesus spoke the words. Now I knew how the servants at the wedding had felt!

In the months since then, Jesus has returned to my village many times. And every time, I have seen Him perform miracles. The last time He was at my home, I was holding the doll He gave me. He looked at me and reminded me that God always rewards faith and trust in Him. But this time, I didn't need to be reminded. I knew it was true!

Today, I'm standing on a hill with my mom and Dohdah. I'm again holding the doll Jesus gave me. This time, He is saying goodbye. He told us He is going to heaven to be with His Father. As I looked up at Him, He smiled. I knew exactly what He was thinking! Have faith and trust in Him! I know how to do that ... because I'm a little one who came.

———————————————————————

More about Ruth

This Ruth is not in the Bible, neither are any of the members of her family. However, the Bible does tell us about a wedding that took place in Cana. Jesus's mother, Mary, had a close relationship with the bride's family and Jesus attended the wedding. And sometime later an official came to Jesus while He was in Cana asking Him to heal his son.

You can read in the Bible about how Jesus turned the water into wine in John 2:1-11 and how He healed the little boy in John 4:43-53.

∽

Yamin watches his donkey's new baby colt stand to
its feet for the very first time.

YAMIN, THE SON OF EPHRAIM

*H*i there! My name is Yamin, and I live in a small village just outside of Jerusalem. I am twelve years old and the only son of a tanner named Ephraim. Tanners treat animal hides so they can be made into sandals, shoes, and clothing. They are also used to make straps and harnesses for animals, skin bottles to carry liquids, and writing materials.

My dad buys his animal skins from the temple in Jerusalem. A temple is where Jewish people gather to worship God. Because of the many animals that are sacrificed as an offering to God each day in the temple, there are many animal skins for my dad to purchase. He sells some of those skins back to the temple after they are treated so they can be used to make Torah scrolls, which are pages containing the first five books of the Jewish Bible. The skins become the pages in the scrolls, and some are made into the straps that fasten the pages together.

Though our work provides an important service to everyone in our region, no one wants to live or work near a tannery. As you can imagine, the skins of dead animals can smell really bad and look pretty gross. So, our tannery and home are located outside of our village, away from the other houses and shops.

My dad is teaching me how to be a tanner and one day the business will be mine. One bad thing about being a tanner is that we soon start to smell just like the tannery – so people don't like to be around us very much. As a matter of fact, tanners are not permitted inside the temple. We do not attend religious celebrations. My dad tells me that years ago tanners worshiped in a separate building. That doesn't happen anymore, but people don't sit near us.

Our tannery consists of two small rooms and a yard. Inside the rooms are tubs made of plaster and stone. Those tubs are filled with different smelly mixtures that we use to treat the animal skins.

Our small stable, where my dad keeps the animals, is located up from the tannery in the opposite direction from the way the wind blows. He uses these animals to pick up untreated skins from the temple and deliver the finished hides to our customers. By keeping the stable upwind, my dad shelters the animals from the unpleasant odors, so they do not smell bad and make his customers sick when he makes deliveries.

Seven years ago, when I was five years old, I became very sick with a high fever. My parents were afraid I was going to die. They prayed and asked God to take away my fever. After several days, the fever did go away … but so did my ability to speak. The doctor told my parents that it had something to do with the fever's effect on my brain. No matter how hard I tried I could not speak any words. I was forced to "talk" by grunting and pointing. Eventually my parents and I developed a sign language we could use for me to "speak" to them.

My parents continued to pray that God would restore my speech, but as the years passed, we all began to lose hope.

I was already separated from the other kids in my village because I was the tanner's son, but it became even worse when I could no longer talk. The donkeys in our stable became my best friends. I pretended they could hear me and understand me when no one else could. And I could understand them, too. We had our own language. Taking care of the animals quickly became one of my jobs. I made sure the donkeys were fed and watered, and their stable stayed clean.

· · ·

Three years ago, our female donkey was pregnant. She had already given birth before to three baby donkeys called foals. Two of her foals had been fillies (female donkeys), and the other one was a colt (a male donkey). Colts and fillies are not fully grown until they are four years old.

Our little mama donkey was expected to give birth soon, so I was watching her closely. Having seen her deliver three times before, I had a pretty good idea what was going to happen. But I was still amazed by the sight of new life. When your home is a tannery, you become used to seeing the skins of dead animals around you all the time. So the birth of a baby animal is a special reminder of how God continues to give life. That's why I had named our female donkey Tikvah, meaning "hope."

Finally the day arrived. It was the time of year when we would soon observe the Passover, one of our special religious festivals. Our expectant Tikvah lay down on her side on the ground. I could tell she was getting ready to deliver her foal. I ran to get my dad. He told me he would only help her if she began to have trouble with the birth. Otherwise, he would leave her alone to do what she already knew how to do. It wasn't long before we could see the baby colt's head. After a few minutes, Tikvah stood up.

About that time, a Man who had been walking by our stable stopped and came over to join my dad and me as we watched Tikvah. He didn't say a word. He just nodded his head at us and smiled.

After a while the rest of the foal's body came out and gently fell to the ground. Tikvah immediately turned around and started licking her new foal to clean him. My dad declared that it was a colt. Even the stranger seemed happy at the sight of this new life. I watched Him as He turned His eyes toward heaven and I heard Him say, *"Father, You are the Giver of life, and Your light lets us enjoy life."*[1]

· · ·

I wished I could have said something right then. I wanted to thank God for this little colt, too. To my surprise, the Man suddenly knelt down in front of me and looked into my eyes. Even though I didn't know Him, I could see a gentleness in His eyes. Somehow, He knew I could not speak. He reached out and cupped my head in His hands and said, "Father, *Your goodness is as high as the mountains. Your justice is as deep as the great oceans. You protect Your people as well as the animals.*[(2)] Glorify Your Son by restoring this young boy's voice."

Suddenly, I knew that God had answered this Man's prayer. My heart was overflowing from the birth of the colt, so the first words out of my mouth were, "Papa, the colt is born! God has given him life!"

I don't know which one of us was more shocked – me, that I could speak, or my dad who had just heard my voice! But our attention quickly turned from the colt to the Miracle Worker kneeling in front of me. Slowly, He stood to His feet. My dad knelt before Him and said, "My

Lord, how can I ever thank You for restoring my son's voice? How can I ever repay You? Praise be to God! My son who has been mute for four years can now speak!"

The Man looked at him and said, "Give glory and honor to the Father who has led Me to you today."

I reached out and hugged the Man. Even though I could talk, I didn't know the words to say to thank Him for what He had just done. But I think the Man knew that because He turned my attention back to the baby donkey. "Yamin, what name will you give to the colt?"

At first, I was surprised He knew my name. My dad had not said it. But somehow this Man seemed to know a lot about me! I had already thought of a name for the colt, so I didn't hesitate. "I will name him Segev, because he will grow up to be great and mighty."

· · ·

"That is a good name for him, Yamin," the Man said, "because one day he will play an important role in the Father's plan." This man even knew things about our colt!

Then He turned and walked away. My dad yelled to the men who were traveling with Him. "Please tell me this Man's name!" One of the men looked back and said, "The Teacher's name is Jesus of Nazareth." My dad and I were still on our knees hugging as we watched Jesus walk away. We didn't know for sure if we would ever see Him again, but something told us we would.

A few days later, I traveled with my dad to deliver a supply of tanned hides to the storage area outside the temple. The hides would be used for making Torah scrolls. I waited outside with the cart and donkey while my dad made his delivery. While I was waiting, I heard some men talking about how Jesus had gotten angry and chased sellers and money-changers out of the temple two days earlier. They said Jesus told them, *"Stop turning My Father's house into a marketplace!"*(3)

. . .

"Who does this Jesus think He is?" one of the men asked. "Who put Him in charge of the temple?"

Suddenly, a boy who was just a little older than I was spoke up. "I think God must have put Him in charge!"

The man who had asked the question began making fun of the boy. But the boy said, "Yesterday I was helping my dad finish the work on the roof of our home and I slipped and fell to the street. Everyone says I was dead. But Jesus was walking by at the time. My dad says He walked over to me lying there on the ground and said, 'Young man, I say to you, rise!' And I sat up. It was as if I had never fallen. Nothing was broken or bruised. I didn't hurt at all!

"My dad says Jesus brought me back to life! And when my dad asked Him how, He said, 'You cried out to the Father for help. He heard your prayer and your son has been made whole. All so that the Father might receive glory!'

"So I know He came from God! That's who put Him in charge!"

I couldn't keep silent, so I said, "Four days ago, Jesus stopped by our stable and healed me. For four years I could not talk, but when Jesus touched me my voice returned. I think God put Him in charge, and we better listen to Him! If Jesus got angry, it was because people were doing something they shouldn't ... and they needed to stop!"

The man continued to laugh at the other boy and me, but the others with him became silent. They knew the boy and I were speaking the truth!

The boy came over to me and said hello. His name was Uriah and he lived here in Jerusalem.

Both of us had been touched by Jesus that week, and our lives would never be the same!

In the years that followed, Jesus became even more famous. We heard people talk about how He was able to make the blind to see, the deaf to hear, the lame to walk – and as I well knew, the mute to speak! We even heard He had raised the dead to life. And I knew it was all true! I would never forget the day He stopped by our stable – or the day I met Uriah!

I'm happy to tell you that Jesus did come back to see us again – just a few months ago. He had a favor to ask my dad. "Ephraim, I need your help. Would you let Me ride into Jerusalem on the back of Segev when I return for the next Passover?"

My dad and I never hesitated. It was an honor for Jesus to ride into Jerusalem on the back of our three-year-old colt! Maybe Segev had been born for this very reason – to bring glory to God. And maybe that's why I was unable to speak for those four years – so Jesus could heal me and bring glory to God!

Today, I'm standing on a hill with my dad. Jesus did ride Segev into the city – and a lot happened after that. But today, we came to say goodbye to Jesus. He told us He is going to heaven to be with His Father. He's finished what He came here to do. He has brought honor to His Father in heaven. He looked over at me and smiled. Then He said that we are all to bring glory to God. We are to follow Him in all that He has taught us. I will do that ... because I'm a little one who came.

———————————————————————

More about Yamin

Yamin is not in the Bible, neither are any of the members of his family or even the other little boy, Uriah. However, the Bible does tell us about a donkey and its colt that Jesus rode into Jerusalem on Palm Sunday.

· · ·

You can read about Palm Sunday and the colt in the Bible in Matthew 21:1-11.

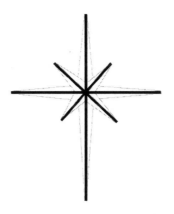

Ilana sits up in bed after Jesus says,
"Little girl, get up!"

ILANA, THE DAUGHTER OF JAIRUS

My name is Ilana. I am fourteen years old and have always lived in the village of Capernaum, which is located along the Sea of Galilee. It is a beautiful place! I enjoy walking and playing with my friends along the sea. Many of the families in our village make their living as fishermen.

I am an only child. My dad, whose name is Jairus, is the chief rabbi (religious leader) of our village's synagogue – a place where Jewish people meet to worship and pray to God. He started that job when I was eight years old. He is a kind and caring man who tries to help everyone, including a very sad woman who also lives in our village named Deborah.

She told my dad that she had been sick for almost twelve years. I could not believe anyone would be sick that long! Her sickness caused her to bleed every day, which made her very weak. Though she was still young, she looked like an old woman. The doctors had never been able to help her. Other rabbis she had seen had prayed for her, but nothing changed. My dad prayed for her, too, but still there was no change.

She didn't have any family living in our village, and I don't think she had any friends. I would sometimes see her buying food from sellers, but most everyone stayed away from her. Sometimes I would pick wildflowers and take them to her at her home. I prayed that God would heal her and bring joy back into her life.

When I was ten, two girls moved to our village with their mom so they could live with their grandma. The oldest girl, Sarah, was twelve, and her sister, Iscah, was nine. Their home was near the synagogue, right next door to our house. We soon became best friends and played together all the time. They told me they had moved to our village because their dad, whose name is Peter, was now a follower of a Man named Jesus. They said Jesus was traveling around Galilee teaching people more about God. I decided He must be a rabbi like my dad.

It wasn't long after I met Sarah and Iscah that Jesus came to visit our village. He was teaching in the synagogue. Even my dad told me that he had never heard anyone teach from the Scriptures like Jesus. He talked about God as if He knew Him personally. But Jesus didn't only teach about God and how we are supposed to live, He also performed miracles. People were saying He could make sick people well.

One day I was in the synagogue with my dad listening to Jesus teach about faith. He had said, *"If you have faith like a grain of mustard seed, you will say to this mountain, 'Move from here to there,' and it will move, and nothing will be impossible for you.*"[1] I couldn't wait to go see Deborah and tell her what Jesus had said.

Just as Jesus finished teaching, Sarah came into the synagogue. She was bringing a message to her dad that her grandma was sick with fever. Her dad asked Jesus if He would go see his mother-in-law. Sarah and I followed our dads as they walked with Jesus to see Sarah's grandma. I kept saying to myself that I had faith like a grain of mustard seed! We all must have had that kind of faith, because when Jesus touched the sick woman's hand, she sat right up like she had never been sick! Jesus had "moved the mountain!"

Later that day when I went to see Deborah, I told her what I had seen Jesus do to Sarah's grandma. I told her that I had faith like a grain of mustard seed that Jesus could heal her, too. She thanked me for my faith but said she no longer believed she would ever be well again. I told her I would have faith for her!

· · ·

An important man in our village is named Shachna. He used to manage the household for our king, Herod the Great, until the king died. Shachna's son, Chuza, is now in charge of the household for our current king, Herod Antipas. Chuza has a son named Samuel who is one year younger than I am. Samuel sometimes comes to our village with his parents to visit his grandpa. Since his grandpa's home is near mine, we often see each other and have become friends.

One day, when I was eleven, Samuel arrived in our village with his parents. When I went to his grandpa's house to see him, his mom told me Samuel was very sick. In fact, they had come to our village to see if Jesus would heal Samuel. However, Jesus wasn't here so Samuel's dad had gone to look for Him. I told Samuel's mom I would pray with faith like a grain of mustard seed for Samuel to be well again. I told her I knew Jesus could heal him. She told me she believed He could, too. But I could tell she was worried. She asked me to ask my dad to come pray for Samuel.

. . .

My dad spent most of that night and the next morning beside Samuel's bed praying for him. My parents did not want me to get sick, so I was not allowed to stay with my dad. My father later told me that he had been afraid Samuel was going to die.

But suddenly, Samuel sat up in bed as if nothing was wrong. The nurse who was helping take care of him checked and said his fever was gone! It was about one o'clock in the afternoon. It was just like the day Jesus had healed Sarah's grandma! But, Jesus was not here this time.

It was the next day before we learned that Jesus had spoken the words to Samuel's father exactly at one o'clock: *"Go back to your son. He will live!"*[2] No matter where we are, if we have faith, Jesus will hear us and answer our prayers!

About a year later, I got sick. My body was burning up with fever. I had no strength. I couldn't even lift my head off my pillow. I could tell my mom and dad were worried. I whispered as loud as I could, "Remember what Jesus said, *'If you have faith like a grain of mustard seed, you will say to this mountain, "Move from here to there," and it will move, and nothing will be impossible for you.'"*(3)

I heard my dad tell my mom, "I just spoke to some of Jesus's followers and they expect Him to return here today."

"Yes, but will He get here in time?" my mom asked.

"He wasn't here when He healed Samuel," my dad said.

"Yes," my mom replied, "but does He even know that our Ilana is sick?"

"I will walk down to the shore so I will be there to get Him as soon as He arrives," my dad told her.

. . .

He leaned down and kissed my cheek. "Have faith the size of a grain of mustard seed," I whispered. I could tell my dad was trying not to cry.

I prayed that God would give my parents the faith and strength for whatever was going to happen. I knew that I might die. But I trusted Jesus no matter what.

As I lay there on my bed, I could hear my mom's soothing voice as she spoke to me. And then, I couldn't hear her anymore. I tried to open my eyes, but I couldn't see her anymore. It was like everything stopped! I wasn't afraid. Everything was peaceful. Time was standing still.

"Little girl, get up!"(4) I heard Him say. It was Jesus! I knew His voice. I opened my eyes. I could see Him, and He was smiling at me. My mom and dad were looking down at me with tears in their eyes. I saw Sarah's father out of the corner of my eye and three other men who were also followers of Jesus. I sat up, just like Jesus told me to do.

Jesus then took my hand and helped me stand up. I walked over to my mom and dad and hugged them. Jesus had healed me, just like I knew He would. I didn't have any fever, and I felt strong again. Everyone else looked at me, and then they looked at Jesus. I walked back to Jesus and hugged Him. When He put His arms around me and returned my hug, I knew I was in the safest place I could ever be – the arms of Jesus.

It wasn't until later that my parents told me what had happened. During that time when everything stopped, I was dead. Even then, without realizing it, I had been resting in the arms of Jesus. Though my parents and others were sad about my death, Jesus told them, "*She's only asleep.*"[5]

.   .   .

He knew I was dead, but He also knew that He was going to bring me back to life. My story was not over. He had let me die so He could bring me back to life and honor His Father. He wanted everyone to know that if we believe and trust God, He can move mountains.

When I walked outside with Jesus, Sarah and Iscah ran up to me and put their arms around me. Everyone was so surprised and began to praise God. My friends and many people I did not know came up and hugged me.

But then I saw a woman coming toward me out of the crowd. She looked like someone I knew. But she looked much younger now. There was a smile on her face. I had never seen her smile before. She was carrying a handful of wildflowers that she gave to me. We hugged each other and began to cry. They weren't tears of sadness; they were tears of joy. Deborah whispered into my ear, *"If you have faith like a grain of mustard seed, you will say to this mountain, 'Move from here to there,' and it will move, and nothing will be impossible for you."*[6]

. . .

Jesus had moved mountains in both of our lives that day! He had healed Deborah of her sickness as she reached out to Him by faith, and He had raised me from the dead. Nothing is impossible with Jesus!

Two years have passed since that day. Today, Deborah and I are standing on a hill with my dad looking up at Jesus. He's getting ready to go up to heaven. Much has happened in the past two years. Jesus even died a few weeks ago. But He didn't stay dead. He rose from the dead, just like He brought me back from the dead. There aren't a lot of us who can say that! God has different plans for each of us. But His plan will always lead to His glory. All He asks is that we trust Him and follow Him with faith like a grain of mustard seed. It's not about our size or our age, it's about having faith. I know ... because I'm a little one who came.

––––––––––––––––––––––––––

More about Ilana

Three of the Gospels record that Jesus restored the life of the daughter of Jairus. The Bible never tells us her name, so the name used in this story is made up. But she was a very real girl with a very real story to tell. Deborah also is not mentioned by name in the Bible. She is referred to as "the woman with the issue of blood."

You can read about both of their stories in the Bible in Mark 5:21-43.

∾

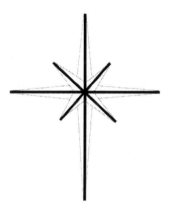

Jonathan gives his loaves and fishes to
Jesus.

JONATHAN, THE SON OF JESSE

Hello! My name is Jonathan and I am eleven years old. My village in Galilee is surrounded by olive trees. My dad once told me that some of the trees are almost two thousand years old. These trees produce the best olives you have ever eaten! The olives and olive oil are sold far and wide throughout our region of the world.

My family is one of the few that doesn't earn a living from the olives. My dad, whose name is Jesse, is a shepherd. He raises sheep and goats. About a year ago, he started to teach me how to shepherd the flock.

. . .

I am my parents' third child. Sadly, both of my older brothers died while they were still in my mother's belly. My parents wanted to always remember them in a special way, so they named my oldest brother Samuel and my middle brother David. We even remember their birthdays every year, and I often think about what they would be like. I wish I could have known my older brothers – to play with them, tell them my secrets, and learn from them. My parents and I talk about the day when we will all be together in heaven.

My mother, whose name is Maacah, tells me that she and my father named me Jonathan because it means "God has given." They knew I was His gift to them. They tell me that I brought joy back into their home and their hearts.

I was just a few months old when they discovered I had been born deaf. Some of our neighbors asked them if God was punishing them. I don't think they meant to hurt my parents with their unkind words, but I know they did. My parents had done nothing wrong. God had a different plan for me, which included being born deaf.

While I was still very young, my mother began to teach me signs I could make with my hands that would stand for words. The first words she taught me were "I love you!" As time passed, my vocabulary of signs grew. Sometimes it was fun knowing that no one else knew what my parents and I were saying to each other … but other times it was hard.

The other boys in our village never wanted to play with me. And when we were with other people, I tried to read their lips, but I wasn't very good at it. And since I couldn't hear, I couldn't speak, so it made it hard when I was around other people.

One or both of my parents was always with me. A few times, my dad took me with him as he watched over the sheep, but he was always afraid something might happen to me when he wasn't looking. Since I couldn't yell for him if I got in trouble, he thought it was safer if I stayed home with my mom.

About a year ago, two strangers came to our village. They told everyone they were followers of a Man named Jesus. My parents told me that one of the men stood up in our place of worship and talked about this Jesus. Many of our people had heard of Him. Some said He made the deaf to hear, the blind to see, and the lame to walk. My mom told me that a prophet from long ago, whose name was Isaiah, had written about a Man who would come and do these things. These two strangers were saying that Jesus was that Man!

My parents talked all that day and night about whether Jesus could help me hear. My dad wasn't sure. He didn't want any of us to be disappointed again. But my mom decided they needed to find out. So, the next morning, after my dad had taken the sheep and goats into the hills, my mom took me to where the two strangers were staying.

My mom asked them if Jesus could heal me so that I could hear. She explained that I had never heard a bird sing, the sound of the wind blow, or even the sound of her voice. She asked, "What do I need to do so that my son can hear?"

One of the men, whose name was Shimon, began to talk to her. I had no idea what he was saying, but later my mom told me he said Jesus had sent the two of them to our village. He had also sent other men to other villages. He told them all to preach the Good News and heal in His name. Shimon told my mom he would pray and ask God to let me hear.

A tear slipped down my mom's cheek as she gently placed her hand on my shoulder and directed me to walk toward the man. I didn't know what he was going to do, but I trusted my mom – so I would trust this man. He placed his hands over my ears. I looked up and could see that he was speaking. All of a sudden there was something different taking place. I was actually hearing sounds! I didn't know what any of them meant at the time, but the man was saying, "… Father, we ask You to unblock his ears and let him hear so that he and his parents, and others in this village, might believe on Your Son, Jesus Christ of Nazareth."

As Shimon took his hands away, I quickly raised my hands to my ears. For the first time in my life I could hear! I excitedly looked at my mom. I didn't know any words to speak, so I told her with signs, "I can hear!" Then she spoke my name, "Jonathan!" I had never heard anyone say my name. I had never heard my mom's voice until that moment!

Suddenly, my mom began to cry tears of joy. She and I hugged for a long time. The two men were shouting praises to God! Quickly the news spread throughout the village. My mom and I left to find my dad. As we ran toward him on the hill, my mom shouted out, "He can hear! Jonathan can hear! God has given him hearing!"

My dad didn't know what to think at first, but when he saw the smile on my face, he wrapped his arms around me, drew me close, looked up to heaven and shouted, "Thank You, God!"

The two men remained in our village for two more days. I went to our place of worship to hear them teach. I wanted to know more about the Jesus who had made me hear, even though I didn't understand most of the words. That would take some time for me to learn – but my parents and others would teach me.

I learned that the man who prayed for me was named Shimon. I learned to say his name – after I first learned to say "Mama" and "Papa!" And then I learned to say "Jesus!" I remained close to Shimon for his remaining time in our village. Though I did not understand his words, my heart told me that he was speaking truth.

A few days after Shimon and the other man left our village, I was on the hill watching our flock with my dad. He was teaching me how to be a shepherd – and we were learning how to talk to each other. Off in the distance, my dad and I saw a large crowd in the valley. Just a little ways up the hill from the crowd was a Man who appeared to be speaking to them. Everyone seemed to be paying close attention. My dad said we were going to lead the flock closer so we could hear what He was saying.

I noticed there was a group of men standing near the Man. Soon I saw that one of them was Shimon! I began to wave to get his attention. When he waved back, I asked my dad if I could go see him.

"Yes, but stay in a place where I can see you and you can see me," my dad instructed. "And take your sack of food with you!" With that, I was off as quickly as I could run. When I arrived by his side, Shimon waved at my dad to let him know I was there and that he would keep an eye on me.

As we sat in the grass, I asked Shimon if the Man speaking was Jesus. He smiled and nodded his head. I didn't understand most of what Jesus was saying. Shimon was able to explain a little bit to me. But I was just happy to be sitting with Shimon and listening to Jesus.

As the afternoon continued, some of Jesus's followers came to Him and said, *"No one lives in this place. Send the people away. They need to find food and places to sleep in the towns and countryside around here."*[1]

But His followers were surprised when Jesus said, *"You give them something to eat."*[2]

I looked at the crowd, and then I looked at Shimon and said, "That's a lot of people to feed!" I may not have known all of my words, but I knew my numbers, and it would take a lot of food to feed this many people.

Jesus turned to one of the men and asked, *"Where can we find bread for all these people to eat?"*[3] The man answered, *"Someone would have to work almost a year to buy enough bread for each person here to have only a little piece."*(4)

The man was surprised when Jesus replied, "Don't look at what you don't have. Look to see what the Father has already given you. *How many loaves of bread do you have now? Go and see.*"(5)

While Jesus and the man were talking, I tugged on Shimon's sleeve and showed him the food my mom had placed in my sack. Though I couldn't understand all of what was being said, I had a pretty good idea, and I wanted to help in any way I could.

Shimon turned to another one of Jesus's followers and showed him my sack of food. The man called out to Jesus and said, *"Here is a boy with five loaves of barley bread and two little fish. But that is not enough for so many people."*(6)

. . .

I didn't wait to hear Jesus's answer. I stood up and walked over to Him to give Him my small sack of food. I wasn't thinking about how little I had. I wasn't thinking about how little it was compared to how much was needed. I just knew that I owed Jesus everything I had. I knew He would know what to do with my food. He smiled and thanked me as He took the sack from me.

Then He looked at His followers and said, *"I tell you the truth. You must change and become like little children. If you don't do this, you will never enter the kingdom of heaven. The greatest person in the kingdom of heaven is the one who makes himself humble like this child."*[7]

As I stood there at His side, Jesus said to His followers, *"Tell the people to sit down."*[8] Once they had been seated, Jesus lifted the sack toward heaven, and gave thanks to the Father for the food … and for my faith. He then began to break the bread into pieces, giving the pieces to each of His followers to give to the people.

They continued to carry the bread from Jesus to the people until everyone had plenty.

Then Jesus did the same with the fish. After everyone had eaten as much as they wanted, He said, *"Gather the pieces of fish and bread that were not eaten."*[9]

His followers filled twelve baskets with the leftover pieces of bread and fish. As the baskets were set side by side, I looked up at Jesus and smiled. Yes, He had known exactly what to do! And I knew from that moment that I would always be able to trust Him! Jesus wrapped His arm around me and told me that He was proud of me. He told me that I had shown everyone there what it meant to have faith. And He told me to continue to trust Him by faith.

Just before He told me to return to Shimon's side, He said, "Tell your parents that Samuel and David are fine. The Father is watching over them, just like He is watching over you. You will see your brothers one day in heaven, and they will see you and your parents. It will be a great day of celebration! And I will be there as well. Until then, Jonathan, follow Me!"

Shimon walked me back to rejoin my dad. We carried two of the baskets of bread and fish and gave them to my dad for our family. Shimon told him that Jesus's miracle had all begun with my kindness. And he said everyone had learned from me that day. Then he said goodbye and returned to join the rest of Jesus's followers.

Over the past year, my dad has taught me a lot about what it means to be a good shepherd. He told me that Jesus is our Good Shepherd. A few weeks ago, He was even willing to lay down His life for us – His sheep – on a cross.

My dad and I traveled here today to see Jesus. We're standing with Shimon on a hill looking up at Jesus. He is getting ready to go up into heaven. He said His work here is done and we are to tell others about what we have heard Him say and do. He told us to tell everyone to trust

Him – just like little children. Then He looked at me and smiled. I know I will see Him again ... because I'm a little one who came.

————————————————

More about Jonathan

Jonathan is not in the Bible. But Jesus did send out seventy-two of His disciples to go into the villages to teach and heal in His name. Also, there was a little boy who gave his food to Jesus to feed the crowd of five thousand men plus women and children.

You can read in the Bible about the disciples who were sent into the villages in Luke 10:1-16 and the feeding of the large crowd in John 6:1-14.

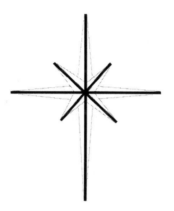

Asher helps remove the burial cloths from Lazarus.

ASHER, THE SON OF AMARI

My name is Asher and I am fourteen years old. I live with my parents in Bethany, a city about two miles from the Mount of Olives in Judea.

My dad, whose name is Amari, takes care of a large vineyard located just outside of the city. The vineyard is owned by a man named Simon, but you probably know him as Lazarus. My dad and Mr. Simon grew up together and are good friends.

. . .

This vineyard is the largest in our region, so Mr. Simon and his sisters, Miss Martha and Miss Miriam, are very rich and live in a big house. Though we live in a smaller house near the vineyard, it is still much nicer than many of the other homes in our city.

My mom often helps Miss Martha in the big house with chores and cooking. Mr. Simon and his sisters aren't married, so there aren't any kids at their house for me to play with. A few of the families that work in the vineyard have children, but most of them are much younger than I am, so I don't have many friends. Most of the time, I help my parents with their work. My dad often tells me to pay close attention, because one day when I'm older I could take over his job, just like he did from his dad.

One night five years ago, I was helping my mom in the big house. Mr. Simon and his sisters had invited the chief priest of our city, whose name is Phinehas, for dinner. He and Mr. Simon are good friends, so he often eats at their house.

After dinner, Mr. Simon called his two sisters and all of the servants into the big room. He even asked my dad to come. Mr. Simon then told us that he was sick with a disease called leprosy.

I had heard of leprosy, but until that moment I had never known anyone who had it. I knew that people who had leprosy were called lepers. It is a bad disease that starts with sores on their skin that will not go away. Then their hands and feet can lose feeling. Eventually their arms and legs can become twisted.

No one is allowed to be around lepers. They have to leave their homes and live out in the desert by themselves or with other lepers. No one knows how to make lepers well again. Sadly, most of them die.

Miss Martha and Miss Miriam were crying very loudly as Mr. Simon told us his news. Everyone else, including my mom and dad, were also very upset. Mr. Simon left that night and we didn't know if we would ever see him again.

One afternoon about two years later, my dad received a message that Mr. Simon was waiting to see him just outside the vineyard. My dad was surprised that Mr. Simon had come back. He knew that lepers weren't allowed to return to their homes. I wanted to go with my dad to see what was going on, but he told me it wasn't safe for me to come and I needed to wait at home.

When my dad returned home, he was so excited. "Simon has been healed!" he said. "He no longer has leprosy! He has been healed by Jesus of Nazareth! And Jesus has given him a new name. He now will be called 'Lazarus' because God has helped him and healed him!"

The next week, Mr. Lazarus's sisters held a big party to celebrate the return of their brother. Most everyone in town came to the party, including the servants.

. . .

Soon after that, Jesus came for a visit. Though Mr. Lazarus and his sisters always treated me like I was a part of their family, I was used to other important people not paying any attention to me. Usually those people would talk to me only if they wanted me to do something for them.

But Jesus was different! I already knew He was the most important person in the world – He had healed Mr. Lazarus! And when I first saw Him, He looked right at me and smiled. He told me to come sit with Him. I was surprised He knew my name. But I found out later that He knows everyone's name, and He knows everything about us. Then He asked everyone else to sit with Him, too.

Jesus began to teach us. He told us He knew that we made our living from the grapes in the vineyard. He said He knew we worked very hard to grow and harvest the grapes. But then He said, "*I am the true vine; My Father is the gardener, and you are the branches. If a person remains in Me and I remain in him, then he produces much fruit. But without Me he can do nothing. Remain in Me and follow My teachings."*[1]

Later, I talked to my dad about what Jesus had said. He told me that just like we were servants of Mr. Lazarus, we all – including Mr. Lazarus – were servants of Jesus. He was the special One that God had promised to send. God created us to produce fruit. That fruit is good works that honor God. But we can't do those good things on our own.

Grapes will only become good fruit if they are attached to the vine. If they are not on the vine they will wither and die. The same is true of us ... and Jesus is our vine. We remain in Him by trusting Him, and following Him ... and following His teachings.

"I want to remain in Jesus," I said to my dad.

. . .

"So do I," he replied.

After that day, Jesus often came to see us, and we were always happy when He came. It didn't matter what else was going on – we would stop what we were doing so we could visit with Him. Even though He had more followers with Him each time He came, Miss Martha would cook a big meal for everyone to honor Him. Miss Miriam usually sat at His feet. Mr. Lazarus always treated Jesus as his most honored guest. We always hated when it was time for our Friend to leave.

A few months ago, Mr. Lazarus became sick and fell to the ground in the vineyard. I helped my dad and two other servants carry him to his home. The nurse came to treat him, but nothing she did made him any better. Miss Martha decided they needed to ask Jesus to come. He was staying in a nearby village, but it would take a whole day before someone could get there to tell Him. My dad told me he was afraid Mr. Lazarus would die before Jesus could come.

· · ·

My dad was right. Later that same day, Mr. Lazarus died. Miss Martha and Miss Miriam cried and cried. It was like the day they learned that their brother had leprosy. But this time, no one could make them feel any better. My mom and dad reminded them that Jesus would be here the next day. His visits had always brought joy. Perhaps this time He would at least bring them comfort.

We all waited for Jesus the next day – but He never came. The person who had taken the message to Jesus returned just before sunset and said Jesus had decided not to return with him. We all believed that Jesus would come the next day – but He did not. Miss Martha kept herself busy cooking meals and making sure all of the guests were cared for. Miss Miriam, however, continued to cry without stopping.

By the fourth day, I wasn't sure how much of Miss Miriam's crying was because of the death of Mr. Lazarus and how much was because Jesus hadn't come. But that afternoon, Jesus arrived. Miss Martha went out to greet Him, but Miss Miriam refused to go. After a little while, Miss Martha came back into the house and told Miss Miriam, *"The Teacher is here, and He is asking for you."*[2]

Miss Martha asked me to walk out with Miss Miriam because she was not yet very steady on her feet. When we got to where Jesus was waiting, she fell at His feet and said, *"Lord, if You had been here, my brother would not have died."*[3] As the last word came out of her mouth, she started to cry again.

A crowd was now gathering around us. Those who had been in the house had followed Miss Miriam thinking she was going to visit the tomb where Mr. Lazarus's body was buried. They were also crying loudly. Jesus interrupted them all by asking, *"Where did you bury him?"*[4]

Someone in the crowd said, *"Come and see, Lord."*[5] At that moment, Jesus began to cry, and He reached down and helped Miss Miriam to her feet so they could walk together to the tomb. I didn't know what I was supposed to do, so I just followed behind them. As we walked, I realized that I had never seen Jesus cry before. At the time, I thought it was because He was sad about Mr. Lazarus's death. But I later learned that He was crying for a different reason.

When we arrived at the tomb, He told someone in the crowd, *"Move the stone that is covering the entrance away."*[6] By then, Miss Martha had also joined us at the tomb, so she spoke up, *"But, Lord, it has been four days since he died. There will be a bad smell."*[7]

Jesus turned to Miss Martha and said, *"Didn't I tell you that if you believed, you would see the glory of God?"*[8] I realized then that Jesus had cried because the people hadn't believed in Him and what He can do – even those who knew Him best, like Miss Miriam and Miss Martha.

As they moved the stone away, Jesus looked up and said in a loud voice, *"Father, I thank You that You heard Me. I know that You always hear Me. But*

I said it out loud because of the people here around Me. I want them to believe that You sent Me."[9]

Then He shouted, *"Lazarus, come out!"*[10]

The entire crowd became silent. We all were shocked that Jesus would say those words. Everyone was looking at the opening to the tomb. It seemed like time stood still, but suddenly something or someone came hopping out. His hands and feet were wrapped in cloth, so he was unable to walk. All he could do was hop. Jesus said, *"Take the cloth off of him and let him go!"*[11]

My dad stepped forward and began to unwrap the cloth. Then I stepped forward to help him. In a few minutes, we had removed all the cloth. There standing in front of us was Mr. Lazarus!

Everyone was shocked! Jesus had just brought Mr. Lazarus back to life. Everyone began to turn toward Jesus and kneel before Him ...

including Miss Miriam, Miss Martha, and Mr. Lazarus.

At that moment I remembered what Jesus had once said to all of us: *"If a person remains in Me and I remain in him, then he produces much fruit. But without Me he can do nothing."*[12] Jesus, the Vine, had produced fruit that day through His branch – Mr. Lazarus. Nothing can separate us from the Vine – not even death!

Several months have passed since then. Evil men put Jesus on a cross. They thought His life had ended the day He died. That's what we had all thought about Mr. Lazarus. But Jesus had plans through His own death just like He did through the death of Mr. Lazarus. And Jesus walked out of His tomb to the glory of His Father in heaven!

My dad and I are standing here on the hill with Mr. Lazarus, his sisters, and a whole crowd of people. Jesus is getting ready to go up into heaven. But He wants us to remember that we are to remain in Him and follow His teachings! "I will, Jesus," I said, "because I'm a little one who came."

More about Asher

Asher is not in the Bible and his parents aren't, either. But we do read about a leper whom Jesus healed. We also read about how Jesus had dinner with a leper by the name of Simon who is called Lazarus elsewhere in the Gospels, together with his sisters, and how Jesus raised Lazarus from the dead. Some teachers believe Simon and Lazarus are the same person. Also, some of you may know his sister Miriam by her Aramaic name "Mary." "Miriam" is her Hebrew name.

You can read about all three parts of that story in the Bible in Luke 5:12-16, Matthew 26:6-13 and John 11:1-44.

Uriah brings a bowl and towel to the upper room just
as Jesus told him to do.

URIAH, THE SON OF YITZHAK

$\mathcal{M}$y name is Uriah. I am fifteen years old and I live in the city of Jerusalem. My dad's name is Yitzhak and he is a fuller and weaver. Fullers clean the wool from sheep and pound it with sticks so it can be made into cloth. They also clean and restore old cloth so it can be reused. Weavers use the wool, as well as flax, to create beautiful woven cloth of all colors, textures, and styles. My dad is teaching me how to become a fuller and weaver.

My ancestors helped Nehemiah rebuild the walls of Jerusalem many years ago. Our shops and home are located near one of the gates called the Water Gate. Our shops are at street level, and our home is above the shops.

When I was twelve, I helped my dad build an upper room over our home. The room is a place where we can host family and friends who come to visit us. We can also rent it out to travelers who come to visit our city during the special religious festivals.

One day, my dad and I were finishing work on the roof of the new room. We were setting the roof tiles in place. I was walking very carefully along the roof line to get some more tiles when my foot slipped. I tried to reach out for the edge of the roof to catch myself, but I missed and fell headfirst onto the street below.

I don't remember what happened next, but my dad tells me that by the time he got to me, I wasn't breathing, and my heart had stopped beating. He said he didn't know what to do, so he called out to God to help me. Right then, a Man knelt beside me. My dad thought He was someone who had traveled to Jerusalem for Passover, one of our Jewish festivals. He and the handful of men who were traveling with Him had been walking by just as I had fallen. He had stopped to see if He could help.

My dad said the Man took me by the hand and said, "Uriah, I say to you, rise!" and I sat up. I remember that! I was sitting on the street. A Man was holding my hand and looking at me. My dad was kneeling right beside Him. I looked at my dad, then I looked at the Man. He looked right back at me and said, "Young man, behold your father." Then He turned to look at my dad and said, "Father, behold your son!"

The Man then stood to His feet, reached down and again took my hand and helped me stand up. Suddenly I remembered what had happened. I had fallen off the roof. I looked up and saw how far the roof was from the ground. But I didn't seem to be hurt. I didn't have any pain, and I didn't have any bruises. It was like I had never fallen. But I knew that I had. How was this possible?

.   .   .

My dad was still there on the ground on his knees looking up at the Man. He said, "Who are You? And what did You do?"

"Yitzhak," He said, "you cried out to the Father for help. He heard your prayer and your son has been made whole. All so that the Father might be glorified."

My dad said, "Sir, how is it You know our names, but I don't know Yours? Even so, I know I have You to thank for restoring my son!"

"Thank the Father for hearing and answering your prayer," the Man said as He reached down and helped my dad to his feet. With a broad smile, He added, "Thank Him for giving you your son once again! And now go, give the boy something to eat."

.   .   .

Then the Man turned and began to walk away. My dad and I just stood there looking after Him. One of our neighbors came to my dad and said, "His name is Jesus. He is from Nazareth."

The next day, I was standing outside the temple (a place where Jewish people worship). A group of men was talking about how Jesus had chased some men out of the temple who weren't supposed to be there. One of the men said, "Who does this Jesus think He is? Who put Him in charge of the temple?"

I surprised myself when I said, "I think God must have put Him in charge!" I then explained what Jesus had done for me the day before. When I finished, another boy just a little younger than I am also spoke up. He told how Jesus had made him speak again. By the time we were both done, the men stopped saying bad things about Jesus and walked away.

Jesus came back to Jerusalem several times after that. Each time He did, He created a lot of excitement in the temple. The religious leaders always tried to put Him down, but each time people would tell stories about how they had seen Jesus correct the religious leaders. And we continued to hear about how He had healed many people – just like me.

Jesus stopped by to see me and my dad on some of His visits to the city. We were always happy to see Him. He often told me how big I was getting, and how I was becoming a young man. He always asked if I was loving the Lord God with all my heart, soul, and mind. He told me that was the first and most important commandment. He also wanted to know if I was obeying my mom and dad, and honoring them in all that I did. He told me that everything He did was to bring honor to His Father.

During one of His visits a few months ago, He asked my dad if He and His followers could use our upper room to celebrate Passover. My dad told Him it was His to use for as long as He needed it.

. . .

Jesus told us He would send some of His followers on the morning before the Passover to make preparations. He asked my dad to have one of his servants meet them at the Sheep Gate and then lead them to the room. My dad said he would have one of his servants carry a pitcher of water so they would know to follow him. I spoke up and asked my dad if he would let me do that, and he agreed.

On the Sunday before Passover began, we heard shouts out in the street. Everyone seemed to be excited. "Jesus is coming!" some were shouting. Others were saying, "Let us go and greet Him as He arrives!"

I asked my dad if I could go and see. "We will all go!" he replied.

When we arrived at the road, we couldn't get close to Jesus because there were so many people. All of them were shouting, "Hosanna!"

which means "Lord, save us!" Others were shouting, *"Praise to God in heaven!"*[1]

We found a place where we could get a little closer. People were laying their coats in the road and others were cutting palm branches from the nearby bushes and laying those in the road to make the rocky road softer. As Jesus got near, I could see He was riding a donkey's colt. He was smiling and waving at the people – just like a friend would.

I shouted to Jesus, and He looked right at me and smiled. I already knew that Jesus was the Promised One. But that day I also knew He was my Friend – and I was so happy that everyone was welcoming my Friend into the city!

I didn't see Jesus again for a few days. But I knew He was in the city. Each day everyone was talking about Him. The crowd in Jerusalem that week seemed more excited about Jesus than they did about Passover.

. . .

Early that Thursday morning, I went to the Sheep Gate carrying a pitcher of water as Jesus had said. I saw the men Jesus had described to me. I could tell they were watching for me. I started back to our house and watched to make sure they were following.

When we arrived, they pointed at the house. Then they pointed at me. They realized that I was the boy who had fallen. I led them straight to my dad. When they saw him they said, *"The Teacher asks that you please show us the room where He and His followers may eat the Passover meal."*[2] My dad told me to take them up to the upper room.

When they arrived, they saw that my dad had already provided them with everything they would need to prepare the meal: fresh eggs from the poulterer, some lamb from the butcher, vegetables and fruits from the farmer, and wine from a local vineyard. The women who were with the men began to prepare the food for the evening meal.

· · ·

Later in the day, Jesus and the rest of His followers arrived. Before He went to the upper room, He stopped to greet my dad and me. He thanked my dad for providing a place for Him to spend this special time with His followers. He asked me to bring a bowl of water and a towel to the upper room and set it by His place at the table. He said He would need them for something He planned to do that night. As I looked at Jesus, I could see that something was different. His smile was missing. He seemed to be very focused on something. I had no idea what it might be.

I made sure that the bowl and towel were there just like Jesus had asked. I got permission from my dad to help serve Jesus and His followers that night for the meal instead of being with my family. This was the first time in my life I had not been with my family to celebrate this important meal.

Before the meal began, all of Jesus's followers were talking and enjoying each other's company. I could tell they didn't think this

Passover meal would be any different from others they had shared together. But all of that changed when Jesus got up, took the bowl of water and towel, and began to wash one of His follower's dirty feet. Suddenly the room became silent and everyone began to stare at Jesus. Even I could tell they didn't know what to do. The Son of God was washing their feet!

One by one, Jesus washed each man's feet. Then one of the men who followed me that morning – the one named Peter – said, "*Lord, are You going to wash my feet?*"[3] Jesus replied, "*You don't understand what I am doing now, but someday you will.*"[4] "*No,*" Peter said, "*You will never wash my feet!*"[5] Jesus replied, "*If I don't wash your feet, then you are not one of My people*"[6]

Peter then said, "*Lord, after you wash my feet, wash my hands and my head, too*"[7] But Jesus corrected Peter and said, "*After a person has had a bath, his whole body is clean. He needs only to wash his feet. And you men are clean, but not all of you.*"[8]

.   .   .

I didn't know what He meant by that last statement. But soon after that, one of his followers got up and left the room. He looked like he had been given a chore to do ... but I didn't think it was a chore from Jesus.

After the main part of the meal, Jesus broke the bread and passed it around to everyone. Then He passed a cup of wine. I knew that both of those things were part of the tradition for this first meal of Passover. But I had never heard anyone say what Jesus said that night. He told the men that the broken bread stood for His body that would be broken, and the wine stood for His blood that would be shed.

Jesus made it sound like He was going to be the sacrifice instead of a lamb. I didn't know what that meant ... and I don't think the rest of the people in that room knew what He meant, either.

After a while, Jesus led them in singing, and then they left. I stayed to help clean up. When I was finished, I went to bed. But I had trouble falling asleep that night. I kept thinking about what Jesus had done and said – and I had a feeling that something bad was going to happen.

The next morning I woke up to shouts out in the street – "Jesus has been arrested! The religious leaders have taken Him to Pontius Pilate! They plan to kill Him!"

That was a little over a month ago. They did kill Jesus! He died that day on a cross and His body was buried in a tomb. I couldn't believe that the religious leaders had killed Jesus. But on the third day, He walked out of that tomb. Later that same night, He appeared to some of His followers in our upper room. When I heard the news, I remembered the day Jesus had told me to stand up. Death could not beat Jesus any more than He let it beat me the day I fell. Jesus has power over death. He has power over everything!

.   .   .

Today, my dad and I are standing here on a hill with a large crowd of people. He's getting ready to go up to heaven. But He just looked at my dad and me and said, "Uriah, behold your father, and Yitzhak, behold your son ... and both of you, follow Me!" I remembered how Jesus had told me to honor my father and now how He had honored His. I knew that I would honor my father and I would honor His Father by following Him ... because I'm a little one who came.

More about Uriah

Neither Uriah nor his parents are in the Bible. But we do read about the upper room where Jesus washed the feet of the disciples and observed the Passover meal. That same room was the place Jesus appeared to His disciples after He arose from the tomb. And it was the room that the disciples waited in after Jesus returned to heaven.

You can read about all four parts of that story in the Bible in Luke 22:7-20, John 13:1-35, John 20:19-23 and Acts 1:1-14.

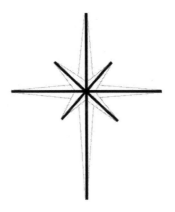

Rachel helps her father as he finishes putting on his
high priestly robes.

RACHEL, THE DAUGHTER OF CAIAPHAS

My name is Rachel and I am fourteen years old. I live in the city of Jerusalem. My father's name is Caiaphas and he has been the high priest of our people ever since I was three years old. A high priest is the top Jewish religious leader, and all the other priests answer to him. My father also leads our Great Sanhedrin, which is the highest court in our land.

Once each year on a religious festival known as Yom Kippur, he is the only person allowed to enter into the holiest part of the temple. While he is in there, he burns incense and sprinkles goat's blood on a special seat – called the mercy seat – as an offering to God on behalf of our people. So, you can see that he is a very important person. I was very proud of my father. He always looked so handsome dressed in his high priestly robes.

My mother is the daughter of my grandfather, Annas, who was the high priest before my father. He is also a very important person. My father and grandfather are able to do pretty much whatever they want to as long as they don't break Roman law. Our Roman governor, Pontius Pilate, is the highest ruler of our land under the authority of Rome. But the governor knows that our people consider the high priest to be our highest leader, so my father and Pontius Pilate are constantly arguing with each other.

When I was ten, a Man named Jesus came to the temple. People said He was a miracle worker and teacher who healed a lot of sick people. He became very popular and most of the people liked Him. But He caused a lot of excitement one day when he chased men out of the temple who He said should not have been there.

Some were men selling their animals to be used as sacrifices. Others were trading Roman coins for temple coins because my father and grandfather told them to do so. Both men made a lot of money from these activities, so you can imagine how mad they were when Jesus chased those bad men out of the temple. From that day on, my father and grandfather said they were going to punish Jesus for what He had done. But they knew they could not punish Him right then, because most of the people agreed with what Jesus had done at the temple.

Every time Jesus came to Jerusalem, He would teach in the temple. And every time He did, my father and grandfather would talk about Him and how they were going to punish Him. One night after dinner, I overheard them talking to our servant, Malchus. Malchus's father had been my grandfather's servant for many years. Malchus had grown up in my grandfather's home, and he and my mother had played together when they were both children. As a matter of fact, after my mother and father got married, my mother asked my father to hire Malchus to manage the servants in our home. Because of his friendship with my mother, Malchus has always looked out for me ever since I was a baby.

That night, I heard my father say, "Malchus, I have a job for you. You are more than a servant to me. You are more like a trusted friend. I know I can depend on you. There is a Man by the name of Jesus who threatens everything that we believe in. He places Himself above the high priest. He causes a lot of trouble. I want you to follow Jesus and listen closely to what He says. I want to know if He says anything that is against our laws – or Roman laws. He is a threat to us and our way of life. He will make a mistake, and I will thank you when you help us catch Him!"

I heard Malchus promise that he would catch Jesus doing something wrong. He said he would find out what tricks Jesus was using to heal people. He promised he would not let my father down. And I knew he wouldn't. He was loyal to my father, and he would find out how to stop Jesus from threatening my father's rule.

A few nights later, I heard Malchus tell my father, "I am sorry to report that I have not seen Jesus do anything wrong. When I spoke to the people He healed, they said He didn't use any tricks. The friends or family who were with them supported their statement that they had been blind, deaf, or lame, and now they were well. And I have not heard Jesus say anything that is against our laws or Roman laws. I even heard some of your scribes (men who knew and protected the law) when they tried to trick Him. But Jesus never lost control. He always answered them with truth."

Then Malchus added, "Are you certain, master, that He is not who He says He is?"

I had never seen my father get so mad. "How could He possibly be who He says He is?" my father yelled. "He is a simple carpenter from

Nazareth. He has no religious training. He has never served in the temple. If He had been sent by God, God would have told me! I am the high priest! And this man threatens my leadership and our way of life. He cannot be the Son of God. There is only one God – and it's not Him! How could you even ask me such a question? Away with you!"

Malchus tried to apologize, but my father didn't want to hear any more. Malchus saw me in the hallway as he left the room. He knew I had heard what just happened.

As the months passed, my father seemed to forgive Malchus. But he did not forget about Jesus. One day, we heard about how Jesus raised a man from the dead. The man had been buried for almost four days! Many people began saying Jesus must be the Promised One, and others were talking about making Him king. My father and grandfather became even more determined to punish Jesus.

.   .   .

I was outside the temple with two of my friends a few weeks ago and heard that Jesus was entering the city riding on a donkey's colt. I had never seen Jesus, so I decided to go watch. My friends and I found a place along the road just in time to see Him pass by. Many people were putting their coats or palm branches on the ground in front of Him to honor Him. Everyone was welcoming Him into the city with shouts of "Hosanna!" which means "Lord, save us!"

As I looked at Jesus, He didn't seem like a threat to me. He looked with kindness at the children walking beside Him. He didn't look like any of the important men I knew. He was dressed very simply, not in fancy robes like the priests. Even His eyes lit up as He smiled. When the priests came through the city, they always tried to keep a distance between themselves and the people. They wanted everyone to believe they were so much better than the rest of the people. Jesus, though, seemed to really like being with the people.

. . .

As He passed by me, He turned and looked at me. His were the kindest eyes I had ever seen. He wasn't just looking at me like I was another face in the crowd. He looked at me like He knew me and was genuinely happy to see me. His look lasted only a moment, but the feeling in my heart lasted much longer. I began to think my father might be wrong. He must not really know Jesus, because if he did he would think differently. Jesus wasn't a threat!

When I got back home, I knew I couldn't talk to my father, or even my mother, about Jesus. I decided to talk to Malchus. I told him what I had seen and how I had felt. He told me that it wasn't a good idea for me to say those things to my father.

Even now, he said, my father and grandfather were setting a trap for Jesus in the temple. It had been three years since Jesus had chased the bad men out of the temple. They had never been allowed to return – until now. My father and grandfather knew Jesus would chase them out again when He returned the next morning.

They were going to use His actions to bring charges against Him before the Sanhedrin.

I asked Malchus if he thought my father and grandfather were right. He told me he was a servant, and I was their daughter and granddaughter. We needed to support their decisions and honor their actions. We could not speak about this again.

Five days later, I woke up very early in the morning. A large group of people were outside our home. The torches they carried lit up the sky, and they were making a lot of noise. I slipped out of my bed and made my way downstairs to see what was going on. I knew my father wouldn't like it if he saw me, so I tried to stay out of sight.

My father had a special room where he always did official temple business. Many men had gathered in that room. As I looked in, I saw my father wearing his priestly robes. He rarely wore those at home. But this time I wasn't thinking about how handsome he looked; instead, I was looking at Jesus standing in front of him. My father looked like he was in charge of a trial.

My father shouted at Jesus, *"Tell us, are you the Christ, the Son of God?"*[(1)]

Jesus answered, *"Yes, I am. But I tell you, in the future you will see the Son of Man sitting at the right hand of God, the Powerful One. And you will see Him coming in clouds in the sky."*[(2)]

His answer made my father really mad. He tore his beautiful robes and said, *"This man has said things that are against God! We don't need any more witnesses. You all heard Him say these things against God. What do you think?"*[(3)]

The people answered, *"He is guilty, and He must die."*[(4)]

.   .   .

Then the other people in the room began to spit in Jesus's face and beat Him with their fists. Others slapped Jesus and said, *"Prove to us that You are a prophet, you Christ! Tell us who hit You!"*[5]

My father told the temple guards to take Jesus down to the basement of our home. They walked right past me as they left the room. Jesus turned and looked at me. This time His eyes weren't smiling. He was sad. But I could tell He wasn't sad for Himself. He was sad for us. My father had just decided the Son of God was guilty!

The only person I knew I could talk to was Malchus. I went to his room and saw he was packing up his few belongings. It looked like he was going away.

"Malchus, what are you doing?" But then I saw there was a lot of blood on his coat. Before he could answer my first question, I quickly asked, "What happened to you?"

. . .

He looked at me and sighed. I could tell he had something important to tell me.

"Last night," he began, "your father told me to go with the temple guards to arrest Jesus. We found Him in a garden on the Mount of Olives with His followers.

"We surrounded Jesus and one of the men who was with Him drew his sword. He was in front of me, just a little to my right. I raised the club I was carrying to knock his sword out of his hand. But the man was faster than I was. The blade of his sword sliced off my ear.

"I dropped the club and reached my hand up to where my right ear should have been – but it was no longer there. It was lying on the ground. As blood poured down my neck, I started feeling weak and fell to my knees. I saw that my coat was covered in blood. My head started to spin, and I knew at any moment I was going to black out.

"I heard someone shout, *'Put away your swords. Don't you realize that I could ask My Father for thousands of angels to protect us, and He would send them instantly?'*[6]

"Suddenly someone was kneeling in front of me. It was Jesus! He placed His hand on the side of my face, and the pain stopped! When He took His hand away, I discovered my ear was back in place – right where it was supposed to be. I was no longer bleeding! At first, I thought maybe I dreamed having my ear cut off. But when I saw my coat soaked in blood I knew I had not made it up!

"Jesus was still there kneeling before me. I looked into His eyes. There I was trying to arrest Him. But He wasn't mad at me – all I saw in His eyes was love. This Man I had hated because I thought He had betrayed my master was anything but bad. He had shown me warmth and forgiveness. He had healed my pain. I mouthed the words, "Thank You." But they didn't seem to be enough.

"It all lasted only seconds, but it changed me. The other men around me looked shocked. One of the soldiers reached down, took Jesus by the hand, and jerked Him to His feet. They tied ropes around His wrists. Everyone who had been with Jesus ran away. Then the guards took Jesus and left. I was left there, kneeling in the garden all by myself.

"I did not know what to do. My master had ordered me to return and report about the arrest of Jesus. But I now knew Jesus was not a threat. My master was the threat. And now I have a new Master, and His name is Jesus. I can no longer stay here. I will go look for Jesus' followers and join them."

I told Malchus what I had seen earlier in my father's special room. I told him I knew Jesus was not a threat, either. He is the Son of God.

We should be honoring Him instead of killing Him. I didn't know what to do. I couldn't go with Malchus because the high priest was my father. But Jesus was now my Master. I decided to pray and ask God what I should do.

Today, I walked to a hill where a large crowd of people were gathered, including Malchus. We're all here to say goodbye to Jesus – at least for now. He's getting ready to go up to heaven. My father and grandfather had Jesus killed. He died the same day as the trial in our home. But Jesus didn't stay dead. Three days later He came out of the grave. He is alive!

I told my father, but he refuses to believe it is true. And he will not allow me to talk about Jesus in our home. But Jesus just said, *"You can be sure that I will be with you always."*[7] Then He looked at me and smiled. I will trust Him, and I pray that one day my father and grandfather will, too. I am asking God to give me the words to say so they will believe in Him … because I'm a little one who came.

More about Rachel

Rachel is not in the Bible, but her father and grandfather are. They were the high priests who led the plot against Jesus and had Him crucified.

You can read about the arrest of Jesus in the Bible in Matthew 26:3-5, as well as 47-68, and Matthew 27:1.

～

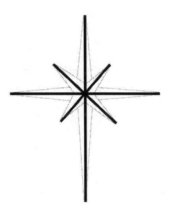

Aquila kneels in the shadow of the cross of Jesus.

AQUILA, THE SON OF PILATE

My name is Aquila, and I was named after my great-grandfather. He helped our Roman government change from being run by a king to allowing our people to choose our leaders. I am very honored to have his name.

I am thirteen years old and I live in the city of Caesarea Maritima. My father's name is Pontius Pilate. He is the prefect (or governor) chosen by our Roman Emperor Tiberius, to govern this region of the world. He rules over the provinces (or states) of Judea, Samaria, and Idumea. I was ten years old when our family moved to this country from Macedonia so my father could become the governor.

Caesarea Maritima is the capital city of these provinces. It is located on the shore of the Mediterranean Sea. It is a port city, which means all of the ships that carry goods to and from this region of the world dock in this port. I have seen ships here from places like Egypt, the island of Crete, Syria, and Rome.

We live in a beautiful palace that was built by the man who used to be the king of this land. His name was King Herod the Great. This palace has so many rooms that I have gotten lost in it!

Even though my father is the ruler of this land, I don't think he likes it very much. I have often heard him tell my mother, Claudia, that the Jewish leaders are hard to get along with. They believe in only one God, and they believe their God is the only true God. They look down on us Romans for our belief in many gods.

. . .

Every day the Jews complain to my father about something – often about something his soldiers have done that has broken one of their religious customs. And when my father demands that the Jewish people do something, their religious leaders tell him they can't because they are observing one of their religious festivals. But, it seems like they are always having a religious festival!

My father gets really upset when the religious leaders won't come into the palace to see him. They say they can't come inside because it would break their religious laws. So, that means my father has to go outside to talk to them when they come to complain! My father really wants us to move to Rome, which is where he grew up. He says it is the most wonderful city in the world!

Several times each year, many Jewish people from all the lands surrounding here travel to Jerusalem for their religious festivals. Jerusalem is where their temple is located. My father goes to Jerusalem during those festivals, too, so he can keep an eye on the people and make sure they don't cause any trouble.

Because my father is such an important man, I don't get to see him as much as I would like. He hired a Greek teacher to live with us so he could teach me math, reading, writing, and science. My mother teaches me about music and art. She is very open to new ideas and has taught me to be that way, too.

We first heard about Jesus soon after my father became governor. He received reports that large crowds were gathering wherever Jesus went. My father was told that Jesus was a powerful speaker and a miracle worker. My father's spies told him that Jesus could make the blind see, the deaf hear, and the lame walk just by touching them or speaking. We even heard that He had brought a dead man back to life!

· · ·

At first, my father was worried whether or not Jesus was encouraging the people to disobey Rome. But, my father's spies told him that Jesus was a religious teacher and He was not speaking against Rome. So, my father decided to leave Jesus alone and let Him keep teaching.

But my father's spies also told him that the religious leaders did not like Jesus. They were afraid that the people liked Jesus more than them. And they were afraid the people would no longer follow them. I was with my father the day he heard that report. He smiled as he said, "Aquila, anyone the religious leaders don't like is most certainly my friend." I wasn't totally sure what my father meant, but I knew it meant that he did not plan to arrest Jesus.

It was seven months ago when I first saw Jesus with my own eyes. My father had gone to Jerusalem because the Jews were celebrating one of their festivals. I was curious about their religion, so I was trying to learn all I could. This feast was about remembering the forty years their people had lived in the desert many years ago. They celebrated how their God had led them through those years and provided for their needs.

I walked to the temple that day to see what was happening. My father always required that my teacher and two of his soldiers go with me whenever I left the fortress. Since I am not a Jew, I am not allowed to enter most of the areas in the temple. But I could still see some of what was taking place inside.

I could see a Man talking to a large crowd standing around Him. I heard someone say, "Jesus is teaching!" I was trying to hear what He was saying when He suddenly stopped talking and looked up. Two guards parted the crowd around Him, followed by two more who were holding the arms of a crying woman. Behind them walked a group of men who were dressed like religious leaders.

The priest who appeared to be in charge said, *"Teacher, this woman was caught having physical relations with a man who is not her husband. The law of Moses commands that we kill with stones every woman who does this. What do You say we should do?"*[1]

The priests all looked at the woman like they hated her. But Jesus looked at the woman like He cared about her. He knelt on the ground and began to write in the sand. I was too far away to see what He was writing.

The priest continued to demand an answer. But when Jesus looked up, He didn't look at the woman, He looked at the priests and said, *"Is there anyone here who has never sinned? The person without sin can throw the first stone at this woman!"*[2]

No one moved. They were all staring at what Jesus had written in the sand. After a few minutes, each one turned and walked away.

. . .

Jesus stood up, looked at the woman, and said, *"Woman, all of those people have gone. Has no one judge you guilty?"*[3] *"No one has judged me, Sir,"*[4] she said. *"So I also don't judge you,"* Jesus replied. *"You may go now, but don't sin again."*[5]

Jesus was not excusing the woman's sin; He was forgiving her. The woman had stood before Him truly sorry for what she had done. But the priests also stood before Jesus as sinners. Jesus knew what was in their hearts. He was reminding them of their sins as He wrote words in the sand. The priests weren't sorry for their sin. They left ashamed – but not forgiven.

I learned a lot about Jesus that day. He was asked to judge this woman. The leaders wanted Him to put her to death. But He judged her fairly and let her go. Yes, she had done something wrong, but that's not why the priests had brought her before Jesus. They were trying to trick Him into doing something wrong. But He would not allow Himself to be tricked by them.

. . .

When I got back to the fortress, I told my father what I had seen. He said, "Jesus was a fool to not let the priests have their way. They will make things more difficult for Him in the days ahead."

Then I went and told my mother. She said, "Jesus did the right thing. He looked at all of the facts and judged her rightly. He would not allow the priests to make Him do the wrong thing. He is a Man of integrity – a Man to be followed."

I thought about my father's answer and then I thought about my mother's. I decided my mother was right … and I decided I wanted to be like Jesus.

Six months later we went back to Jerusalem for the Jewish celebration of Passover. They were celebrating how their God had saved them from death many years ago through the sacrifice of a lamb.

. . .

It was very early on Friday morning. I was still in bed, but I heard shouts and the sounds of a large crowd outside. I looked out my window. There were a number of temple guards walking in front of the crowd. Two of them were holding Jesus's arms. He was in chains and was walking between them. Behind Him was the high priest and other religious leaders. They were asking my father to come out to speak with them.

I decided to walk out on one of the roofs so I could see and hear what was going on. I saw my father talking with them.

The high priest said, *"We caught this Man telling things that were confusing our people. He says that we should not pay taxes to Caesar. He calls Himself the Christ, a king."*[6]

I knew my father didn't believe that. He asked Jesus a few questions, then he turned to the religious leaders and said, *"I find nothing wrong with this Man!"*[7]

· · ·

But the priests insisted. They replied, *"But Jesus is making trouble with the people! He teaches all around Judea. He began in Galilee, and now He is here!"*[8]

I knew my father didn't believe that, either! My mother joined me on the roof. "I just sent your father a message," she said. I told him, *"Don't do anything to that Man. He is not guilty. Today I had a dream about Him, and it troubled me very much."*[9]

My father had the power to set this innocent Man free. He knew that Jesus had not done anything wrong. Suddenly, I remembered that day at the temple when Jesus had stood for truth and what was right. I hoped my father would do the same.

But instead of making the right decision, my father left the decision up to the crowd. *"What should I do with Jesus, the One called the Christ?"*[10] he asked them.

·   ·   ·

"*Kill Him on a cross!*"[11] the crowd roared back.

My father knew it was wrong, but he would not stand up for what was right. He sent for a bowl of water to wash his hands in front of the crowd as he said, "*I am not guilty of this man's death. You are the ones who are causing it!*"[12]

The people yelled back, "*We will be responsible for His death!*"[13]

Tears began to flow down our cheeks as my mother and I watched. We cried for Jesus. An innocent Man was being put to death. But we also cried for my father. He had been afraid to stand up to the crowd. The blood on his hands could never be washed away by the water from that bowl.

It was a turning point in my life. Until that moment, I would have followed my father anywhere. But now, I knew that I would follow Jesus anywhere – even to the cross.

. . .

Soon the soldiers led Jesus away to be hung on a cross and left to die – but not until they had first beaten Him. They beat Him so badly that when they led Him out of the fortress He no longer looked like Himself. His body was bloody, beaten, and bruised. They had placed a crown of thorns on His head.

I snuck out of the fortress without anyone knowing, wearing a coat so I would blend in with the crowd. My teacher and soldiers were not with me on that walk as I followed Jesus from a distance.

I watched as they nailed Him to a cross like He was a criminal. Despite the terrible things the people shouted at Him as He hung on that cross, Jesus put up with it all. He put up with the pain of His beatings. He put up with the pain of their hateful words. He put up with the cross.

. . .

About the middle of the day the sky turned dark. It was like God in heaven couldn't watch anymore. A few hours later, Jesus said, *"It is finished"*[14] and He lowered His head and died. I heard one of the soldiers in charge say, *"He really was the Son of God!"*[15]

As I stood there looking up at Jesus, I thought about the first time I saw Him – kneeling on the ground, writing in the sand. As He hung there on the cross, He had known all of our sins – those of the religious leaders who accused Him, those of the soldiers who had beaten Him, those of my father who had turned his back on Him, and … mine as I watched Him. But just like that day in the temple, He had not come to judge us. He had come to save us.

Today I'm standing on a hill outside of Bethany. My mother is by my side. We're not dressed in our royal robes but in regular clothes. We have decided to follow Jesus. His story didn't end on that cross. Three days later Jesus rose from the dead.

· · ·

A large crowd is gathered to say goodbye to Him – until we see Him again in heaven. He has told us to tell others about Him. I can do that … because I'm a little one who came.

————————————————

More about Aquila

Aquila is not in the Bible, but his father Pontius Pilate is, as is the story of the woman who was brought to Jesus in the temple.

You can read in the Bible about the woman in the temple in John 8:1-11. You can read about Pontius Pilate in Luke 23:1-5 and 13-25. And you can read about the crucifixion of Jesus in Luke 23:26-49.

∾

Naomi and her grandpa see that the stone has been
rolled away and the tomb is empty.

NAOMI, THE GRANDDAUGHTER OF JOSEPH

*H*i! My name is Naomi. I am nine years old and I live in the town of Arimathea located in northern Judea. My dad's name is Matthias and he is the oldest son of my grandpa Joseph.

My grandpa no longer lives in Arimathea. He now lives in Jerusalem because he is a member of the Great Sanhedrin, which is the supreme court of our land. My grandpa is a wise and godly man who seeks to honor Jehovah God in all that he does.

. . .

Our family owns a lot of land around town that is used by many farmers to grow grains and vegetables. They are called tenant farmers, and they pay money to our family to grow their crops on our land. My dad and my great-uncle, Jonathan, oversee our family business for my grandpa.

I like living in Arimathea. It is a quiet town, free of all of the noise and busyness of the big city. There are no Roman soldiers here. As a matter of fact, there are no Romans at all! Everyone knows everyone else! It's like having a great big family. The hills are a beautiful color of green most of the year. The temperature is comfortable – not too cold and not too hot. We get most of our rain during the winter months. The rain fills our wells and springs to carry us through the drier summer months. My grandpa often says that he really misses living in Arimathea.

My best friend is Adina, and we are the same age. Her father, whose name is Ashriel, is our town's rabbi (religious teacher). When Adina and I were both six years old, my grandpa came to Arimathea to visit her dad. Several other religious leaders from Jerusalem came with him. One of those leaders was the high priest! And another one of them, an older man, used to be the high priest. Everyone was so excited that these important men had come to our town!

My grandpa knew that Adina was my friend, so he took me with him for the visit with her dad. She and I played together outside while the grownups talked inside the house. We could still hear some of what they were saying.

"Why did Simeon believe the baby he saw was the Promised One?" one of the men asked our rabbi.

"Who is Simeon?" I whispered to Adina. "And who is the Promised One?"

. . .

"Simeon was my dad's great-grandpa," she whispered back. "And when my dad was a little older than we are now, he would help his great-grandpa walk around the temple in Jerusalem.

"I'm not exactly sure what this means," she continued, "but my dad told me the Promised One is someone God promised to send to save the Jewish people from their enemies."

We listened to more of the conversation inside the house.

"He never doubted that the day would come," Adina's dad replied to the older man. "Even though it had been almost one hundred years since God had given him the promise that he would see the Promised One before he died, his faith was as strong that day as it had been on the day God had first given it to him.

"That morning, when he saw the parents and the baby, he just knew! He told me to help him walk over to the baby. He walked faster the closer we got. He told me his heart was pounding in his chest. As we approached the family, Papa asked if he could see the baby. I'm sure that seemed strange to the baby's parents, but they kindly turned their young Son so Papa could look into His eyes. Tears began to stream down his cheeks! I'll never forget his words when he looked up toward heaven and said, *'Lord, I am Your servant, and now I can die in peace, because You have kept Your promise to me. With my own eyes I have seen what You have done to save Your people.'*[3]

"The baby's mother didn't say a word. She simply smiled at my great-grandpa. I was struck by her tenderness. I could see why Jehovah God had chosen her to be the mother of His Son. When Papa reached to pick up the baby in his arms, she willingly handed the tiny bundle to him.

"The baby didn't cry or make a sound as Papa held Him. Rather, the baby seemed to be looking right into my great-grandpa's eyes. It was as if the baby knew him. And I was sure the baby did know him!

"Papa handed the baby back to His mother and blessed her and the father. We stood there watching as the mother and father walked away with their baby. Papa turned to me and said, 'The people here in the temple have no idea that they have been in the presence of the Son of God.'

"Papa died not long after that. But he died knowing his lifelong mission was complete."

"Did they tell you the baby's name or where the family was from?" one of the men asked Rabbi Ashriel.

"No, they did not," he replied, "and we never asked."

. . .

The older man continued to ask more questions as my grandpa and the others listened. I wasn't sure what they were talking about. As long as I could remember I had heard about the Promised One – the One who would be sent by God to save our people. It sounded as if Adina's great-great-grandpa had seen Him when he was a baby. And if that were true, the baby would now be grown. My grandpa and these other important leaders must be looking for Him. This was all so exciting!

When they finished talking, I left with my grandpa. The other men headed back to Jerusalem, but grandpa stayed with us for a few days.

"Grandpa, has the Promised One come?" I asked.

"I think He may have come," my grandpa replied. "I have met a Man whose name is Jesus. I think He may be the Promised One. I am not sure yet. That's why we came to ask Rabbi Ashriel our questions."

"Do the other men think Jesus is the Promised One?" I asked.

"One of them does, my friend Nicodemus, but the other men don't," he answered.

"Then I will pray and ask Jehovah God to show them," I replied.

"Out of the mouth of a little one …" my grandpa said. But I wasn't sure what he meant.

Three years passed. Each time I saw my grandpa, I would ask him if God had shown the men that Jesus was the Promised One. Finally one day, my grandpa said, "He has shown me, and I am now one of His followers. But right now I am a secret follower."

. . .

By then everyone had heard of Jesus. Even I believed He was the Promised One, and I hadn't even seen Him yet! "Then I'm one of His secret followers too, grandpa," I said.

There are many stories of how He healed people. And a few weeks ago, in the town of Bethany, He called out to a man whose dead body had been in the grave for four days, and that man walked out of the tomb alive! Only the Son of God can do those things!

This year, my dad told me that I could go with him to Jerusalem for the celebration of Passover. This was my first time to go with him. We would stay with my grandparents, and he told me that Jesus would be there. I was so excited!

Two days after we arrived, there was a lot of shouting in the streets. People were running and saying, "Jesus is coming!" I asked my dad if we could go see, and he said we could. People were crowded all along the road. Jesus was riding a colt and there was only enough room for Jesus and the colt to fit through. His followers were walking in single file behind Him. My dad picked a palm branch off a nearby bush and handed it to me. "Wave it in the air!" he said. And together we shouted, "Hosanna!" as Jesus rode by.

I have never been in a crowd that large. I cannot imagine how Jesus felt being surrounded by all of those people who were shouting at Him. I had decided He probably couldn't see any of us in that great sea of people, but I think – for just a moment – He looked at me … and He looked into my eyes. His were the kindest and gentlest eyes I have ever seen. As I looked at Him, a feeling of peace came over me. Then He continued along the road, but the feeling stayed with me.

When we got home, I told my grandpa that I had seen Jesus and explained how I felt. He told me that was how he felt whenever he saw Jesus, too.

. . .

A few days later, I again heard people running and making noise in the streets. This time they were shouting, "Jesus has been arrested! The high priest has taken him before Pilate!" My grandpa told my dad and me to stay in the house. He would find out what had happened and come back and tell us.

Grandpa returned a few hours later. His head was bowed. He was very sad. "Pilate has declared Jesus guilty and He has now been nailed to a cross on the hill outside of town," my grandpa told us. "My friend Nicodemus and I tried to convince the religious leaders to stop this foolish behavior, but we failed. And now that Pilate has issued His death order, there is nothing that can be done to reverse it, short of an order from the Roman Emperor himself.

"Jesus has been whipped and beaten. He will die today on that cross unless Jehovah God sends His angels to stop it. But I don't believe He will do that! Jesus tried to tell us. He once said, 'The

Son of Man must suffer many things. He will be rejected by the Jewish elders, the leading priests, and the teachers of the law. The Son of Man will be killed.'[1]

"This is what He said would happen. Many of the other members of the Sanhedrin are now at the hill watching Him die on that cross. I could not bring myself to go there! I have come home to pray and cry. I cry for Jesus. I cry for His mother and His followers. And I cry for our people. God has sent His Son and we rejected Him! His blood will forever be on all of our hands!"

I knelt beside my grandpa, and I cried and prayed with him.

At noon, the sky suddenly turned black. It looked like the middle of the night. Grandpa told me it was a sign of the punishment that would come to our people for what was being done to God's Son.

· · ·

But then my grandpa said, "Jesus also told us, *'After three days I will be raised from death.'*[2]

"I am sure His family and His followers have not thought about where Jesus's body will be buried. I will go to Pilate to ask permission to bury Jesus's body in my new tomb. The other religious leaders will not like it! I will no longer be a secret follower of Jesus. I will be risking all that I have – my position, my influence, and my wealth. But He is worth it all!"

"I will go with you and help you," my dad told him. "I can't be a secret follower of Jesus anymore, either."

"Neither can I!" I said. "I want to go with you. I want everyone to know that I am His follower."

My dad started to tell me that little girls shouldn't go to the place they were going. But grandpa interrupted him. "Jesus once said, *'Let the little children come to Me. Don't stop them. The kingdom of God belongs to people who are like these little children.'"*(3)

The three of us went to the place where the Roman governor was staying to ask his permission. Pilate came outside to speak to my grandpa. My dad and I stood there silently while my grandpa talked to him. Pilate seemed to be surprised that a religious leader was asking permission to bury Jesus's body.

He told my grandpa that He did not believe Jesus was guilty of anything. He said Jesus was only being killed because that is what the other religious leaders wanted. He acted like he wanted grandpa to tell him he was not responsible for Jesus's death. But grandpa did not do that. Pilate was guilty for what he had done!

Once Pilate had given my grandpa the official paper granting him permission to bury the body of Jesus, we went to a shop in the city to purchase cloth to wrap His body. Then grandpa took my dad and me to the tomb where Jesus's body would be placed. He told us that the place where Jesus was hanging on the cross was no place for a little girl to go. He did not want me to see Jesus like that. He told us to wait at the tomb, and He would return with Jesus's body.

A few hours later, grandpa returned with his friend Nicodemus and another man who was called Simon the Cyrene. The man from Cyrene was carrying the body of Jesus.

They had already wrapped Jesus's body in the cloth we purchased, so I could not see His body or His face. As Simon placed the body in the tomb, I began to cry. I remembered what Jesus had said: *"After three days I will be raised from death."*[4] But I cried because of what they had done to Jesus.

Three days later, a woman arrived at my grandpa's door early in the morning. Grandpa said her name was Mary Magdalene. She was a follower of Jesus, too. We could tell she had been crying, but her tears were tears of happiness. *"I saw the Lord!"*[5] she said. "He's alive! He has said that we are all to gather in the upper room tonight."

The day passed so slowly. I had never wanted nighttime to come so quickly. I couldn't wait to see Jesus! My grandpa, my dad, and I were some of the first people to arrive at the room that night. An older boy named Uriah showed us to the room. As some of the others arrived, they excitedly told us how they had seen Jesus.

Then suddenly, Jesus appeared. He didn't come walking through the door, He just appeared in the room. He said, *"Peace be with you!"*[6] Then He showed us the holes in His hands where He had been nailed to the cross. As I looked into His eyes, they were the same eyes I had seen just one week before. But today, I was different because I was no longer a secret follower – everyone knew I loved and believed in Jesus!

. . .

Jesus smiled at me and said, "Naomi, I am so glad that you came."

Today, I'm standing on a different hill outside of Bethany with my grandpa, my dad, and a crowd of people. Many of them were in the upper room with us the night Jesus appeared. Now we are all here to tell Him goodbye. He is going to heaven to join His Father. But He promised we will see Him again. Until then, we are to tell others about Him. I will do that because I am no longer a secret follower ... I'm a little one who came.

_____

More about Naomi

Naomi and her father are not in the Bible; neither is Adina nor her father. But the stories they all tell are true.

You can read in the Bible about the day Simeon (Ashriel's great-grandpa) saw the baby Jesus in the temple in Luke 2:25-35. You can read about Joseph of Arimathea (Naomi's grandpa) in John 19:38-42.

And you can read about the day Jesus returned to heaven in Acts 1:1-11.

PLEASE HELP ME BY LEAVING A REVIEW!

∼

i would be very grateful if you would leave a review of this book on Amazon. Your feedback will be helpful to me in my future writing endeavors and will also assist others as they consider picking up a copy of the book.

To leave a review, go to:

amazon.com/dp/1734934565

Thanks for your help!

∼

THE COMPLETE EYEWITNESSES COLLECTION

BOOK #1

Little Did We Know

... Eyewitnesses to the Advent

This book is a collection of twenty-five short stories written for adults and teens for the Advent season from some familiar and some not-so-familiar people. Experience the truth of the glorious arrival of the baby in the manger through the lens of these fictional, first-person accounts of the prophecies and events heralding the birth of Jesus.

Available through Amazon

ALSO AVAILABLE AS AN AUDIOBOOK

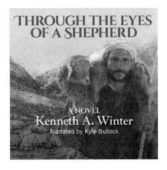

SCRIPTURE BIBLIOGRAPHY

~

The story line of this book is taken from the Bible – specifically from the Gospels according to Matthew, Mark, Luke, and John. Certain fictional events or depictions of those events have been added.

Some of the dialogue in the book is a direct quote from the Bible. Those places are *italicized* in the book and have a number after them. If you want to see where those statements are in the Bible, the reference is listed below.

Also, you will find numbers where the words are not italicized. Those references are to help you better understand some of the statements that have been made in the book. The Bible is the best place to read more about them!

From the author

[1] Mark 10:14-15

[2] Romans 3:23

[3] John 3:16

[4] Luke 19:10

[5] 1 John 1:9

1. Sarah, the daughter of Simon Peter

[1] Luke 5:5

[2] Luke 5:8

[3] Luke 5:10

[4] Matthew 21:21-22 (paraphrase)

[5] Mark 10:15

[6] Mark 6:50 (ESV)

[7] Matthew 14:28 (ESV)

(8) Matthew 14:29 (ESV)

(9) Matthew 14:30 (ESV)

(10) Matthew 14:31 (ESV)

(11) Matthew 21:21

2. Ruth, the daughter of Salome

(1) John 2:10 (NLT)

(2) John 2:4

(3) John 4:48

(4) John 4:49

(5) John 4:50

3. Yamin, the son of Ephraim

(1) Psalm 36:9 (NCV)

(2) Psalm 36:6 (NCV)

(3) John 2:16 (NLT)

4. Ilana, the daughter of Jairus

(1) Matthew 17:20 (ESV)

(2) John 4:50 (NLT)

(3) Matthew 17:20 (ESV)

(4) Mark 5:41 (NLT)

(5) Mark 5:39 (NLT)

(6) Matthew 17:20 (ESV)

5. Jonathan, the son of Jesse

(1) Luke 9:12

(2) Luke 9:13

(3) John 6:5

(4) John 6:7

(5) Mark 6:38

(6) John 6:9

(7) Matthew 18:3-4

(8) John 6:10

(9) John 6:12

6. Asher, the son of Amari

(1) John 15:1, 5, 7

(2) John 11:28

[3] John 11:32

[4] John 11:34

[5] John 11:34

[6] John 11:38-39

[7] John 11:39

[8] John 11:40

[9] John 11:41-42

[10] John 11:43

[11] John 11:44

[12] John 15:5

7. Uriah, the son of Yitzhak

[1] Matthew 21:9

[2] Luke 22:11

[3] John 13:6

[4] John 13:7

[5] John 13:8

[6] John 13:8

[7] John 13:9

(8) John 13:10

8. Rachel, the daughter of Caiaphas

(1) Matthew 26:63

(2) Matthew 26:64

(3) Matthew 26:65-66

(4) Matthew 26:66

(5) Matthew 26:68

(6) Matthew 26:52-53 (NLT)

(7) Matthew 28:20

9. Aquila, the son of Pilate

(1) John 8:4-5

(2) John 8:7

(3) John 8:10

(4) John 8:11

(5) John 8:11

(6) Luke 23:2

(7) Luke 23:4

(8) Luke 23:5

(9) Matthew 27:19

(10) Matthew 27:22

(11) Matthew 27:22

(12) Matthew 27:24

(13) Matthew 27:25

(14) John 19:30

(15) Matthew 27:54

10. Naomi, the granddaughter of Joseph

(1) Luke 9:22

(2) Luke 9:22

(3) Mark 10:14

(4) Luke 9:22

(5) John 20:18

(6) John 20:19

∼

ACKNOWLEDGMENTS

I do not cease to give thanks for you ....
Ephesians 1:16 (ESV)

to my wife, life partner, collaborator and best
friend, LaVonne,
for your willingness to take the risk and walk
the journey;

to my family,
for your support and encouragement;

to Carley,
for putting yourself out there to be used by God
in such a great way and, in doing so, bringing
glory to Him;

to Sheryl,

for helping me craft the stories of the ministry
and passion of Jesus for a younger audience;

to Dennis,
for always having a fresh eye and a willing heart
to bring glory to God;

and most importantly
– **our Lord and Savior Jesus Christ** –
without whom there would be no story to tell.

~

ABOUT THE AUTHOR

 **Ken Winter** is a follower of Jesus, an extremely blessed husband, and a proud father and grandfather – all by the grace of God. His journey with Jesus has led him to serve on the pastoral staffs of two local churches – one in West Palm Beach, Florida and the other in Richmond, Virginia – and as the vice president of mobilization of an international missions organization.

Carley Elder is the talented artist who created all of the beautiful illustrations in this book. You can see more of her gifted work in *Not Too Little To Know*.

To read Ken's weekly blog posts and see information about the other books he has written, go to kenwinter.org.